Who's who

in

GRUNTY FEN

Brief lives of hidden heroes who
made Grunty Fen what it is today

Christopher South

Who's Who in Grunty Fen

Edited by Carol Carman
Designed by Martin Carman
Typing by Janet South
Spelling by Eunice Turkentine

First published in 2015 by Grunty Fennery

ISBN: 978-0-9930130-1-0

An address for Grunty Fennery can be found via the 'Contact Us' section of the website http://www.dennisofgruntyfen.co.uk/shop/ or email info@dennisofgruntyfen.co.uk

Printed and bound in Great Britain by Book Printing UK
Remus House, Coltsfoot Drive, Peterborough, PE2 9BF

By the same author:

The Authorised Guide to Grunty Fen

'Like a modern Marco Polo, the intrepid Mr South has made
startling discoveries in an almost unknown region'
The Sightseer

'Makes paying an actual visit quite unnecessary
or, indeed, desirable'
The East Anglian Wayfarer

'Grunty Fen will never have a better guide than this'
Mrs Olwyn Slant

For recordings, memorabilia and more about Grunty Fen
please go to www.dennisofgruntyfen.co.uk

The author wishes to express his gratitude to his wife,
to Miss Edwards, to Carol and Martin Carman
and a multitude of informants in the fens.

This book is dedicated to the memory of
Pete Sayers.

Contents

Contents (cont.)

INTRODUCTION

Preparing this first attempt at a Who's Who of Grunty Fen has been a reminder of how, when armed with the powerful new Hubble telescope, astronomers directed their gaze at a small area of the sky which had hitherto appeared totally empty. They were astonished to find this "empty" sky was full of many thousands of previously invisible galaxies with incalculable millions of stars, planets and satellites. Encouraged in their search, the astronomers then swivelled the telescope through 180 degrees and scanned another equally empty small window in the heavens. Again they found an equally crowded cosmos.

So it has been with this first attempt at exploring the rich human history of an area long held to be of no interest to serious students of human endeavour. So blinkered has been the popular view of Grunty Fen that seeking the truth has not been easy. The surviving scanty documentary evidence has been largely discarded. A document containing important information about one heroic figure in this volume was found lining a budgerigar's cage in Little Downham and unique back issues of The Grunter parish magazine had been used as pipe lagging, after they had earlier served as wrapping in a mobile fish and chip van.

Fortunately, the oral tradition is strong and the author is grateful to those many local people who have contributed their recollections. We are left to reflect that if scratching the surface of a disregarded community has produced such riches, what might we discover if we swivelled our telescope? For this collection is far from exhaustive. It is offered as a tentative beginning to exploring the galaxy of greatness at Grunty Fen.

Christopher South
Crass Combust
Summer 2015

Who's Who

in

GRUNTY FEN

BARRY "BARMY" BARNARD, The Rev.

(1937-1990)

Ditch inspector, visionary and calendar reformer

It is an injustice to his memory that the "Barmy" soubriquet unkindly accorded Barry Barnard in life should survive his death when so many of those very innovations for which he was mocked have successfully survived and have become part of Fenland life and language.

It was Barnard who invented the famous "V" nozzle for bicycle pumps making it possible to inflate two tyres simultaneously. He also developed a technique for using clear starch for floppy flowers which is still used by pansy arrangers.

The multi-character fancy dress outfit he devised with his mother, Muriel, had only limited success. Operated by tugging at any one of ten different strings, the protean garment left the wearer open to abuse from mischievous merrymakers at a ball. Although arriving as, say, Robin Hood, the vexed owner of a transuniformeral outfit might in the course of the evening appear, in whole or part, as Bo Peep, Henry VIII or Joan of Arc.

Working his way up from manual dredger 4th class, Barnard was such a conscientious and trusted inspector of ditches that when other ditch inspectors fell ill, his foreman would often assign him to stand in for the absent man and inspect strange ditches he had never seen before.

Thus it was that one day in April 1958 Barnard was inspecting ditches at Much Harm, many miles from his familiar

working area. As he gazed round at those strange gullies he was suddenly struck by a feeling of familiarity, as if he had inspected them before, even though he had no memory of having visited Much Harm in his life. That evening he related his curious experience to older members of his family who confirmed his conviction that he had never previously visited

Barry "Barmy" Barnard.

Much Harm.

The following day, a Sunday, he spent his day off returning to Much Harm and the ditch where he had had his curious experience. A gang of boys were playing in the ditch and to his surprise and consternation he felt certain he had seen them before and they, too, acknowledged him with cries of "Wup!", the local greeting to visitors. Yet when he questioned the boys they said they had never seen him before although he "looked familiar".

Back home that evening he strove to dismiss the puzzling

2

incident as a trick of the mind but his sleep was disturbed by a dream in which he found an egg-whisk on a shelf in "The Jericho", the closet at the end of his garden path. Now, his wife had lost her whisk fully three weeks earlier and both of them had long exhausted themselves searching every conceivable place where an egg-whisk could have been lost. The meat safe, the copper and the broom cupboard were scoured in increasing desperation and the couple had prepared themselves for the day when they would have to buy a new whisk.

Rising in the small hours and fired by the dream haunting his head, Barnard almost ran down the path to the little shed and there, above the door on the shelf which was never used because any article stored there tended to fall on a user's head when closing the door, was the whisk! Triumphant and holding the whisk like an Olympic torch, Barnard ran back to the house, shook his wife awake and they spent the rest of the night trying to fathom how the whisk got there. Each denied the remotest possibility of personal culpability but were equally confident the involvement of a third party was impossible.

In the following months Barnard became a changed and troubled man. Ditch inspection requires total concentration for long periods but Barnard's thoughts constantly wandered off to the events of those three fateful days when he found the boys and the whisk.

Great seekers after the truth often have eureka moments –
such as Saul on the road to Damascus, Newton sitting under an
apple tree – and so it was with Barnard. Suddenly he saw it all. He
was not going mad. He *had* been to Much Harm before. He *had*
indeed put the whisk on the shelf! In what was to become the
equivalent of Stephen Hawking's pursuit of a Grand Unified
Theory of Everything, he realised that many other unexplained
phenomena commonly experienced by all of us could be easily
understood if we accepted that the week has not seven days but
eight.

According to Barnard's new calendar, by which many Fen
folk now live, the standard week runs Sunday, Unday, Monday,
Tuesday, Wednesday, Thursday, Friday, Saturday.

By some force of nature, we are unable to remember the
events of an Unday. Mankind lives and goes about its business on
Undays but is forbidden forever from remembering what it did on
that day. That slice of cold pie missing from the larder sometime
between Sunday and Monday was eaten on Unday. That otherwise
inexplicable graze on one's skin was suffered on an Unday. That
stranger towards whom one feels an unjustified antipathy is
because of something he or she said on an Unday. That strange
sense of sadness or gladness we sometimes feel for no good reason
springs in fact from the events of Unday. All strangenesses, all
mysteries, all odd dreams and curious happenings, and, above all,

that impression one has of having "been here before" are down to Unday.

Very occasionally, like the memory of a dream that slips like over-cooked salsify through our waking fingers, we get a vague, glimmering glimpse of our lives on the real second day of the week. Then for a fraction of a second we peer through the veil that blinds us to the true state of our lives.

Granted this vision, Barnard did what all Grunty Fen people do when struck by a new idea: he founded a new religion, known popularly as The Whiskers, but more formally as The Second Day Searchers.

Of the hundreds of places of worship dotting the fens, The Whiskers' chapels are by far the smallest. Each is a small shed accommodating a single soul but up to twelve are grouped in circles a little like Stonehenge. On Mondays, the successors of the Rev. Barry preside at a table in the centre where lies the "Holy Whisk". At a word from the priest all Whiskers open their chapel doors and stare fixedly at the table while a choir of boys standing in a sacred ditch sing appropriate songs. Similar circles can be found over a wide area.

The type of egg-whisk that led to a revolution in the fen calendar.

The sighs, the moans and groans of the straining faithful can

5

be heard at some distance as they strive to remember what they did the day before. Any successes are recorded in *The Book of Unday* together with any tangible supporting evidence. A proposal to publish *The Book of Unday* to enlighten the wider world has been abandoned because, in the words of Mrs Avis Mansfield, Keeper of the Book, many of the memories were "too risqué".

The Rev. Barnard would have agreed. As he himself wrote:

> *"The world may not be ready for a revelation of what it gets up to on Undays"*

and on his deathbed he admitted that he sometimes got a very slight hint of why he took the whisk into the closet but this glimpse was never committed to *The Book of Unday*.

ARNOLD BAZELEY (1919-2001)

Explorer

While the majority of people born in the Grunty Fen area are content to spend their entire lives travelling no further than Stuntney or in the more restless cases, Ely, there is a wanderlust gene in their blood which manifests itself in a rare line who are born with their eyes on far horizons.

So it was with Arnold Bazeley, one of the greatest in a long line of Fen explorers going back to the legendary Wanda Aetheling who discovered Dire Pits in c.900 AD. Bazeley followed his father in the pitch-tosser's trade but from an early age became restless in the spring. Each April he bade his family farewell and with a small sack of liquorice allsorts flung over his shoulder and his trusty bagging hook through his belt set out on foot he knew not whither.

In old age he published an evocative memoir, *Far Afield Afoot in the Fens*, telling how he stumbled across many hitherto unheard of villages and recorded their local customs. There is a sense of wonder in his words as he describes, for example, Great Sorely where the people washed every day and bathed at least once a fortnight or Bastardy where women with large feet were thought especially desirable and baby girls' feet were cruelly clamped between boards from birth to flatten and expand them.

He writes most nostalgically of how, with vast areas of the fens still unpenetrated, and forced by age and infirmity to abandon his travels, his mind was haunted by

> *". . . the unforgettable sound of an elderly Bastardy woman hurrying barefoot at dusk through shallow mud in search of dabchicks' eggs for her simple supper. The slip-slop-slap of her magnificent naked feet and the anxious cries of the dabchick live long in the memory."*[1]

Great Sorely and Bastardy, like so many of the villages Bazeley discovered, can no longer be found. Quite simply, the fen has, as local people testify, "sucked them in". Today's tourist will search in vain for Bazeley's Upper Torment or Patchy Grazing, Curr's Terdly or Bishop Fingering and the extravagant spring fertility rites practised at long-lost Spike Tracey will never be witnessed again until, in some unpredictable eruption of the fen, these settlements re-emerge, are resettled and begin another stage in their episodic stories.

Arnold Bazeley,
restless and fearless explorer.

It is a comfort to know that Bog Bazeley (named after the great man), Slew, Mange, Crass, Feverditch, Gaze Oargy, Dastardly and the quaintly named Brazen Malpractice still survive, reportedly much improved by such technological advances as stock cubes and candles. However, they are now visited only by courageous and wealthy tourists who journey in one of the costly all-terrain security convoys which occasionally venture out. For most of us, the rich cultural landscape opened up by the brave Bazeley must be for the armchair traveller.

8

AUGUST BURTON, Dr. (1917-1997)

Epidemiologist

A small memorial tablet in the porch, or sometimes the north-west aisle of St Judas' Parish Church in Grunty Fen (see *The Authorised Guide to Grunty Fen* p. 12) bears witness to the heroic efforts of this devoted physician to stem the scourge of the green flux, a disease which has cursed the area throughout recorded history and probably beyond.

In the *Annals of Ely* we find references to the greene fluxx, the great flucks, the foul fluxings, the fine flucus and several other variations but the symptoms are always the same. Although no description of this pestilence is needed here, those Latinists with an interest in mediaeval horror may consult *De Rerum Horribilis Fenii Eliensis,* available as a pamphlet at Grunty Fen Post Office or from the patients' book trolley at Grunty Fen Cottage Hospital. Suffice it to say that, as its name suggests, the green flux involves an uncontrollable flux of green matter from the wretched victims. An outbreak in late December among pickers can cause havoc in the Brussels sprout season although some otherwise penniless single mothers have been known to drag themselves out into the fields even when their flux is in full spate to earn enough to buy little

9

luxuries, like a bar of soap or a toy for their children's Christmas stockings.

It was observing this curious phenomenon that first alerted Dr August Burton to the possibility that the disease might have an inherited component. If women struggled to work while their lamentable condition raged and if, as is still commonly accepted, the flux is highly contagious, transmissible in the air, by bodily contact and through bodily fluids which are, in the later stages, copious, why did the disease not occur in Cambridge, Ely or other centres of population to which the Grunty Fen sprouts were consigned at Christmas? Why were those who dined on fen sprouts on Christmas Day not laid low on Boxing Day?

Dr Burton's first endeavour was to identify certain members of the local population who never caught the flux even in the most serious epidemics, and then keep them in total isolation except for the company of one flux victim.

To test the validity of his theory he needed to know that his "guinea pigs" were not related by blood. Sadly, this seemingly simple step presented unsurmountable problems. At first he believed people were reluctant to discuss their ancestry because it was a matter of shame, a case of "skeleton in the cupboard"; eventually he had to accept that most people, even those keen to assist his research, could not specify their parentage simply because they did not know, although almost all claimed some consanguinity with Gabriel "Bad Boy" Goodenson (see *The Authorised Guide to Grunty Fen* p. 59).

Thus his research came to naught, was abandoned and never resumed. Since green flux is unique to the relatively small population of Grunty Fen, none of the major pharmaceutical companies has yet sought a cure. The flux rages on.

Local general practitioners can still offer patients no relief other than a costly sip of Howlet's Elixir, made from the minced bile ducts of albino shrews, which has yet to be approved by the National Institute of Clinical Excellence but still sells well at the Post Office Stores despite its prohibitive price (a complete course is equivalent to the value of 50 railways sleepers or 100 nets of sprouts at today's rates; see *The Authorised Guide to Grunty Fen* p. 68 for more information on currency).

Dr Burton also made a valiant attempt to cure Spew's disease which had been an affliction of childhood for generations, but his research became redundant after Grunty Fen Post Office Stores started selling sherbet dabs. Whether it was the liquorice, the sherbet or the paper casing which improved the children's health was never established, but fen mothers now ensure that their offspring are given their daily dab until they reach majority.

One disease for which Dr Burton did successfully find a remedy was "The Slants" which caused the sufferers to lurch to one side without warning and for no apparent reason.[2] Just as it is

De Rerum Horribilis Fenii Eliensis, available at Grunty Fen Post Office or from the patients' book trolley at Grunty Fen Cottage Hospital. Latin scholars may find this pamphlet particularly upsetting and are advised to have a suitable receptacle to hand when reading.

The young Dr August Burton.

possible to cure a squint by forcing the lazy eye to work in the opposite direction, Dr Burton found that it was possible to cure The Slants by first determining the angle, severity and direction of the slant and then for male patients, weighting their opposite trouser pockets with lead shot. Afflicted females had the elastic of their knicker-legs weighted in a similar fashion to correct the ambulatory fault.

In 1997 Dr Burton fell ill and rather than seek other medical help he decided to heal himself. He started writing a paper about his condition for the *British Medical Journal* but expired after the introductory paragraph, leaving no clue as his symptoms or failed treatments. The cause of his death was given as "Burtonitis" of which he is the only recorded victim.

CUTHBERT BUTTRESS (1894-1954)

Inventor

Born into a well-to-do bantam-plucking family, Cuthbert Buttress showed little talent in the family business but applied his mind from an early age to devising ingenious mechanical devices to ease labour or speed work. Well ahead of his time, he became obsessed with the conservation of energy and the search for renewable sources of power.

Much as James Watt, pioneer of steam power a century earlier, had his moment of inspiration when watching a kettle boil on the hob, Cuthbert Buttress's epiphany came when stroking the family pet dog, Nelson, so named after it became blind in one eye when the local Scout troop were playing tug-of-war with a strand of barbed wire. Despite his handicap, Nelson was an incorrigibly cheerful creature with a long, powerful and ever-wagging tail. Watching this constant wagging one day while listlessly plucking a bantam for his father, Cuthbert thought how much easier his task would be if he could harness the limitless energy of Nelson's tail.

His first experiment was to tie an egg-whisk to Nelson in an attempt to convert the lateral movement of the tail to the rotary movement of the whisk but the dog's tail quickly became inextricably tangled in the whisk blades, much to Cuthbert's father's fury on finding dog hairs in his cocoa.

Undeterred, Cuthbert persevered with a long series of experiments over several years and several dogs, with his mother's irritation made worse when he harnessed the egg-whisk power conversion unit to a pair of clippers she used to trim her husband's beard. Cuthbert wanted to make decorated edges to pie-crust pastry and remove bobbles from a woollen Union Jack cushion-cover his mother had knitted for the front room to mark the Coronation of Edward VII. The dog's tail hair became so

14

cemented into the clipper blades with pastry and cushion bobbles that the apparatus seized up completely and had to be soaked in the inspection pit at Potts Garage (see *The Authorised Guide to Grunty Fen*, p. 46) for most of that autumn.

None of this defeated Cuthbert who pressed on with his experiments even on honeymoon, when one of his more bizarre attempts to harness wasted energy resulted in the marriage being dissolved a few months later.

Still he persevered but, after more than thirty years and almost as many breeds of dogs, he had to admit all his work had led to one unsolvable problem.

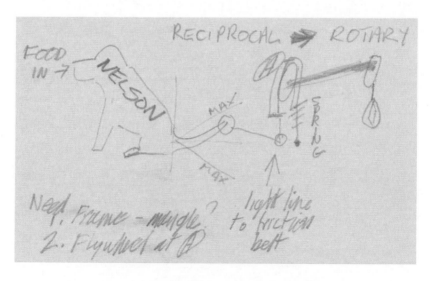

*One of Cuthbert Buttress's earliest designs
to harness the power of a dog's wag to drive an egg-whisk.*

To put it in simple, layman's terms, a dog with a whisk tied to its tail is an unhappy hound and reluctant to wag. To get even one wag by fondling the animal's ears required more digital energy from the fondler than the tail whisk could ever produce.

Like so many great thinkers in the quest to turn base metals into gold or the search for sufficient everlasting free energy, he had struck a brick wall of seeming impossibility.

He died a bitter, frustrated and lonely man. Lonely because no-one could live with a man who kept flea-bitten dogs for the purpose of harnessing the power of their back legs when scratching their ears. He lies now in Grunty Fen churchyard where his headstone epitaph has been made indecipherable by passing dogs.

Cuthbert Buttress assessing the potential of generating energy from pigs' ears.

16

AUSTIN CHALLIS

Poet

While almost the entire works of John Clare, the Northamptonshire "peasant poet", have survived and are in print, only fragments remain of Clare's Fenland counterpart, Austin Challis. Indeed, it is only by the merest chance than we know his oeuvre at all.

By great good fortune a workman demolishing a small hut at the end of the garden at Challis' birthplace in Little Guttering found sheets of yellowed paper covered in handwriting and hung from a rusting hook in the wall, apparently by the poet's wife who had scant respect for his flair. So it is that his admirers have spent years piecing together lines and verses – rudely torn into squares and crudely pierced at one corner – in an effort to make sense of his original intentions.

The Grunty Fen Society for the Improvement of Poetry and Land Drainage was formed in 1952 and has since pursued the task of retrieving what has come down to us.

Austin Challis.

17

Even in its fragmentary state it is easy to see that, like Clare, Challis found his inspiration in the minute observation of nature and everyday life in the countryside. Thus, in one of his most famous verses, couched in his own coarse argot, we find the poet moved by the sight of a strand of rat droppings on the pristine white surface of a sack of wheat flour lying open on the floor of the village bakery:

> *Like a flight of vagrant birds*
> *On this floury poke**
> *Find a skein of ratty ******
> *Enough to make me choke*

* poke = sack (dialect)

Challis also found poetic inspiration from recollections of his childhood, as in *The Classroom* and *Spring Song:*

The Classroom

> *My master grim said he'd grin*
> *If his test I failed to pass*
> *Take his nine-tailed willow whip*
> *And tan my small, bare *****

Spring Song

> *With Easter cheeks bright as apple*
> *In bonnet gay off to chapel*
> *The boys all decked in Sunday best*
> *Mother's cut off their winter vest*

From the fragments of his work that are left, it seems that nothing and no-one escaped his eye:

Carbolic

John has washed himself all over
Smells like a dog that rolled in (?clover)

A Night Out

Then off to the pub to get plastered
Meg's Dad's the worst, the silly ****

But perhaps Challis's most famous and most sensitive lines were written later in life when he reflected on his place in creation and his nation's role in the world. Typical of this, his final period of creativity are *To a Frog* and the poignant *Dear Bird*:

To a Frog

Hallo there, you little green hopper
The French would eat you for their supper
But being English I prefer to tread
On you and confine myself to bread

Dear Bird

Farewell sad swallow of the summer sun.
I hope you don't get shot in Spain
By some peasant with a gun
But survive to fly back here again

ANTOINETTE CLAYDEN (1941-)

Artist

Miss Antoinette Clayden, a tobacconist's daughter who moved to
Grunty Fen from Putney in 1961 when she inherited a modest sum
and resolved to spend her life in rural contemplation, has long been
the foremost figure in what has been described as "The
Enlightenment of the Fens".

She and a small but active group of ladies have in recent
years attempted to "civilise the people" by introducing villagers to
art, literature, folk dancing and crafts. Her campaign has suffered
many setbacks, not least the purchase of a dozen flat-pack spinning
wheels which, when the assembly directions were followed, turned
out to be nests of occasional tables, leaving cynics to suggest
Grunty Fen now has more tables than it has occasions.

However, it has been her work with the local library service
that has placed the greatest demand on her resolve.

The county council library service struggled for many years
to serve Grunty Fen but eventually abandoned the attempt in the
hard winter of 1985. There was no shortage of local people using
the local library in the village hall every Monday and Friday at all
seasons but it was noticed that even a brief cold snap produced a

huge extra demand for books, especially big ones. Unfortunately, very few if any were ever returned.

The County Librarian's theory on the subject is a matter of public record[3]. Even in the village itself there were some protests over the uses to which library books were put in cold weather. Miss Eunice Turkentine, a teacher at the village school, was horrified to find sewn into the bodices of some infants as extra insulation pages of "quite unsuitable sensational novels".

The consequent closure of the county library was a signal for Miss Clayden to abandon her artistic knotted wall hangings and feed Grunty Fen's appetite for culture in another way. She appealed for all villagers to pool their literary resources and contribute their own books to form a new lending library open every day.

An account in the parish magazine, *The Grunter*, records that at the successful opening ceremony the books available on loan from the non-fiction shelves included: *Cooking with Parsley, The Annals of Highland Agriculture – 1905 vol. III, Pony Trekking in Dagenham, The Memoirs of Wilfred Pickles vol. IX, Teach Yourself Swahili, One Hundred Ways with Cod, The Observer Book of Moss, The Goat in Sickness and in Health* and, on the fiction shelves: *Maisie has Triplets, Abandoned Woman, Art Cupboard Love, Bandage Me Tightly, She Was Only Teasing, Salome's Secret* and *Naughty Nuns*.

But the religious shelves offered the widest choice with titles ranging from *Satan's Tribe* to *The Loins of Beelzebub, Witchcraft is my Craft, The Lashing of Lucifer, Eternal Agony* and *Why the Faithful are Doomed.*

This independent lending library went well until the first cold spell in November when all the books were taken out and none returned.

Miss Clayden returned to her loom after she had been presented with a book of thanks signed by all the library users. Sadly, the book vanished before she could get it home.

"Spirals of Love", one of the folk artworks of Antoinette Clayden.
She has rejected several offers for the piece, saying that it
"holds too many precious memories to ever part with it."

CHANTERELLE[4] CODMONGER (1931-)

Musician and folk dentist

Miss Chanterelle Codmonger remains one of the best-known and most feared of fen figures but the artistic activity upon which her fame was chiefly founded was dealt a death blow by changes in the materials used in motor car manufacture.

She was the first female of her line to follow the family calling of dentistry whose techniques and surgical apparatus have been handed down through many generations unaffected by the NHS. While trundling her dentistry wheelbarrow between fen villages, Chanterelle ceaselessly scoured the roadside verges for metal hub caps which often used to become detached from the wheels of passing cars, vans and, more rarely, lorries.

There was a benign purpose in this apparently eccentric behaviour, for pre-plastic hub caps had a resonant quality when struck by a heavy implement like a dental hacksaw or molar hammer drill. By playing what were at first the most basic little tunes on the caps when arranged in a primitive scale of four or five notes, the dreaded dentist could beguile fearful patients, whose lives were haunted by merely imagining the ominous rumble of the iron-wheeled dental barrow approaching across the fen.[5]

All but the most fearful patients found solace in the little melodies coming from what, as time went by, developed into the Hubbophone.

It soon became apparent the Hubbophone was a triple blessing – not only did it sooth suffering but it reduced the need for expensive and largely ineffective anaesthetic and, for those patients who failed to respond to the music, made their groans inaudible to others waiting in the queue for treatment. Miss Codmonger became adept at playing the instrument with one hand while conducting even the most complex surgical procedure.

Things were going well and other musically inclined people in many villages started to build their own Hubbophones. Humber and Standard Vanguard caps were particularly sought-after for their deep sonority and a few fortunate players incorporated Bentley, Jaguar, Alvis and even Rolls Royce hub caps in their ensembles. Riley, Austin, Morris, Ford and Wolseley were acceptable but

The rumble of Chanterelle Codmonger's dental barrow has patients gathering at the local shop in Bleak Fen.

24

Lagonda hub caps were especially valued for their wistful timbre.

Sadly this great aesthetic movement had a built-in flaw as even the most robust luxury metal hub cap was relatively flimsy when used to play *The William Tell Overture* or *The Entry of the Gladiators* with a heavy spanner. Bent and crumpled hub caps never ring true and after a while *Away in a Manager* sounded much the same as *Knees Up Mother Brown* even in the skilled hands of maestro Chanterelle herself.

The need for replacement hub caps led to a dramatic rise in thefts. Car owners who parked on public places often returned to find their caps gone. Gangs of music enthusiasts swooped on Cambridge, ransacked academical car parks and returned to their fen fastnesses with enough caps to build an entire orchestra. The city became known as "The Hub of Crime".

Miss Codmonger pleaded with offenders to cease these raids but eventually it was not her entreaties but the motor industry which produced the solution. As metal caps were replaced by cheap plastic substitutes the whole musical life of the fens went into a decline from which it has never recovered.[6]

In the 1950s and 60s Cambridge rag and bone men were often held up by gangs of thieves demanding hub caps.

The originator of the Hubbophone still gives occasional concerts on the last working Hubbophone (her version of the *March to the Scaffold* from the *Fantastic Symphony* of Berlioz attracts wild applause) but her name is now mainly associated with pain rather than pleasure.

DAISY DOCKERILL (1934-1981)

Pharmacist

In the years immediately after the foundation of the National Health Service, hospitals were gradually re-equipped with more modern beds. The old iron bedsteads were sold as scrap metal and it was this that led to the creation of the Dockerill pharmaceutical empire which flourished briefly at a time when Grunty Fen people were deeply suspicious of any free service and had set their faces against the NHS believing it to be a trap. "The only place you can live for free is a prison" is still a local maxim.

Daisy Dockerill was married to Daniel, an enterprising scrap merchant who lived at nearby Spleen but had his yard at Grunty Fen because the people of Spleen, unlike those at Grunty Fen, objected to living near "such a hideous monstrosity". Grunty Fen people greeted the scrapyard because it attracted strangers and so brought trade.[7]

Mrs Dockerill worked as book-keeper at the scrapyard and often noticed that on windy days the old hospital bedsteads stacked outside her office shed made a curious rattling sound "like Edmundo Ros's maracas" as she said at the time. One day during her lunch break she decided to investigate the mysterious sound and, taking a heavy iron bedhead, she removed the top part from the legs into which it slotted and was astonished to find the bedhead full of pills, tablets, capsules and lozenges of every size, shape and shade.

She called Daniel and together they carried the bedhead into the office and turned it upside down. The pills poured out on to the floor in two rainbow heaps about nine inches high. After staring at each other in amazement they emptied the end from the same bed and found that it, too, was full of medicaments. For the rest of the day all other work was set aside as they brought scores of bedheads and bed ends into the office to disgorge their varied and remarkably well-preserved pharmaceutical contents.

It was Daniel who solved the mystery of how the pills came to be there but it was Daisy who had the inspiration for what to do with them. Daniel realised that for decades during the working lives of the old beds, patients reluctant to take prescribed medicines found a way to dispose of them when eagle-eyed matrons, sisters and nurses had their attention momentarily diverted. Working together, patients quickly eased a bedhead apart, jettisoned their dosage down a hollow iron leg and when asked "Have you taken your pills?" would falsely claim they had. Since most patients recovered quite well anyway, the medical staff's suspicions were never aroused.

During the next month whenever trade allowed, the Dockerills emptied thousands of pills from hundreds of beds. Then, while Daniel concentrated on selling the beds as ideal fencing materials (they can still be seen round the gardens and fields of Grunty Fen), his wife sat on the office floor patiently sorting a mountain of pills into jam jars by size, shape and colour. She said later that the little white ones were hardest because they all looked alike so she "had to lick them to tell them apart by taste".[8]

This done, she set about testing their properties before offering them for sale to local people with their various ailments. As a Sunday School teacher she had thought of feeding them in very small quantities to her divinity class when teaching them about the miraculous manna or the Feeding of the Five Thousand, but in the end settled on her chickens. Keeping meticulous records and careful watch, she noted which pills put them off lay, started a moult or improved their wattles and egg production. It was only after weeks of thorough testing that she dared to devote a corner of the scrapyard shed to a pharmacy.

The free NHS having deterred patients from going to see a doctor for a year or more, there was a huge backlog of cases eager to pay up and swallow down. The results were startling. Grunty Fen had never been so healthy. Even green flux cases diminished (see August Burton, *q.v.*).

This rival medical service was so successful and so popular that Daisy ran out of pills in six months and had to close down the pharmacy. By that time she and Daniel had made enough money to close the scrapyard and retire to a chalet bungalow at Good Thrashing which they called *Dundosing*.

From the pages of The Bugle: an advertisement for the short-lived but highly profitable dispensary which was the brainchild of Daisy Dockerill.

RUFUS FLACK (1795-1855)

Entrepreneur

Grunty Fen people are not noted for their interest in the wider world, preferring the peaceful pleasures of their own quiet dykes and drains. Rufus Flack was an extraordinary exception. Even in a metropolitan setting he would have been seen as an entrepreneurial live wire. In Grunty Fen he was an unparalleled phenomenon.

Inheriting a flooded gravel pit at the age of seventeen, he immediately cast around for ways to turn it into a money-making project. This was at a time when taking the curative waters at inland spas was reaching its height and insignificant small towns all over Europe earned fame and profit by cashing in on the supposed health properties of a local spring. From Harrogate to Tunbridge Wells, inland holiday resorts mushroomed. News of this

*Rufus Flack,
founder of Grunty Spa.*

fashionable industry reached young Flack who promptly declared his flooded pit to be Grunty Spa.

Even quite modest advertising attracted a genteel clientele who arrived in their carriages from Cambridge and as far as Bury St Edmunds and then, having

30

immersed themselves in the dubious waters, went home as Flack could not offer the overnight accommodation that would encourage longer stays and make Grunty Spa a resort to rival Bath.

By happy chance he met in an Ely hostelry an impoverished Prickwillow medical man, Dr Emmanuel Carspite-Weller, lately returned from an unsuccessful attempt to establish a bathing-machine business at Whippham-juxta-Mare on the Norfolk coast. Carspite-Weller's money and hopes had been lost when an unusually high spring tide claimed not only his bathing machines but Whippham-juxta-Mare. However, his faith in the curative properties of outdoor bathing was undimmed and a little later he published a pamphlet not only extolling Flack's therapeutic pit waters but also recommending long periods of fresh air for every sort of disease from acne to xylophonist's wrist. The pamphlet attracted great interest among liverish gentlefolk wishing to avoid the expense of a train journey as far as Yorkshire.

Carspite-Weller's experience gave Flack the inspiration he needed to resolve his accommodation worries. Soon taking a dip at Grunty Spa and spending the night in one of the wheeled shepherd's huts Flack had caused to be parked around the pit proved both attractive and comparatively inexpensive.

The spa was thriving when history caught up with the enterprise. The green flux, that morbid malady which has been the curse of Grunty Fen for centuries and lingers till this day, chose the moment of Flack's greatest success to strike. The epidemic proved especially pernicious to spa visitors who, although this was not understood at the time, had no antibodies, unlike the local people some of whom can shrug off a dose of green flux without missing a day's carrot-scrubbing (see August Burton, *q.v.*).

Undeterred by this setback, Flack rented out his flooded pit for the then-popular mass baptism of converts to various local sects and also to farmers for the disposal of fallen stock during recurrent outbreaks of swine fever, poultry palsy and mange.

But he was ever conscious of the need to replace the spa with another scheme that would capture the popular imagination and offer cheaply and conveniently what people in the outside world could not afford to do or were too timid to try. Once again the answer was in the news: the public prints were full of reports of the discovery of gold in far-flung corners of the world. Paupers were becoming millionaires overnight. Flack, by another happy chance, struck gold in his pit.

News that nuggets had been found in Grunty gravel spread rapidly across the fen. Local men and lads who longed to join a gold rush but whose wives or mothers would not let them go, or who, never having been further than Ely, were daunted by travelling thousands of miles by land and sea, leapt at this opportunity to go gold mining and be home for supper. For a shilling a day plus the rent of a shovel and pick if necessary, they could stake a claim and dig as deep as they dared.

However, the immediate outcome of a month's nugatory nugget hunting was that a number of young ladies from the poorer parts of Cambridge who had heard reports of the role of women in the rowdy saloons of the Klondike and elsewhere set up their own facilities on the fringes of the pit to the profound horror of every woman in the entire Grunty Fen area, to say nothing of the vicar, the Rev. Sternly Boothby-Barktrup.

Flack, who had come to a business arrangement with the ladies, could not hope to prevail against such opposition forces. He closed down his goldmine as he had closed down his spa. He spent the rest of his life living in one of the shepherd's huts still remaining from the spa days and ceaselessly racking his brains for some way to make a profit from the pit. Sadly, he died just before the craze for boating came in.

All that remains of Rufus Flack's Grunty Spa:
the site of the Reception Vestibule, where gentlefolk would be welcomed
before they partook of the waters of the flooded gravel pit.

33

RON "FLASH" GORDON (1965-1994)

Postman and sportsman

The elm, the oak and the ash, the beech and the birch are trees close to the hearts of English people but on the fen, after centuries of ceaseless search for free kindling, even a clump of purging buckthorn is a rarity.

In the absence of great trees the fen folk have long turned to another massive feature of the landscape – the electricity pylon. Mistrustful of the novelty of electricity many villagers have refused to be connected to the mains, preferring coal and paraffin as their main energy sources. Yet they lie under a cat's cradle of high tension lines carrying thousands of volts and are comforted on misty nights by the buzz of discharge as the pylon tops are wrapped in low cloud. Indeed an entire system of weather forecasting is based on how many pylons the observer can see down the grid line before they vanish in mist or a fen blow of rich earth and carrot seed spiralling skyward in spring.

But perhaps the most notable contribution these mighty pylons make to local life is in the field of sport and the greatest name in pylonic sports is that of postman Ron "Flash" Gordon.

Since so few of the people in his Grunty Fen area either

wrote or received letters and then as now eschewed contact with official agencies, Ron Gordon found he had a good deal of spare time on his hands. Just as boys in wooded areas naturally climb trees, the young Ron climbed pylons but never, even as a lanky teenager, got beyond the impenetrable thicket of barbed wire which girdles each leg of a pylon. Never, until the world of pole-vaulting was opened up to him shortly before he was due to leave school and start work.

It was the first time that the English education system had captured his imagination and fired him with ambition. In his last summer term he hurled himself into pole-vaulting with almost obsessive determination and in the autumn he forsook formal education forever and sought out a job that would enable him to fulfil himself.

Encouraged by his father, also Ron, who had been a noted dyke-jumper in his time, young Ron devoted almost every waking hour to mastering the art of pole-vaulting over the barbed wire so that he could climb the pylon beyond the safety barrier.

A pylon stretches up into the wide fen sky; note the barbed wire to deter pyloneers.

Trampyloning, the sport involving a trampoline slung between the four legs of the pylon, is also discouraged.

Many were the wounds he endured, many the setbacks when a tiresome number of Christmas card deliveries interrupted his training. But on March 12th, 1994, a date enshrined in Grunty Fen history, he finally in one giant leap flung himself high over the lacerating wire and clung to the grey girder above wearing round his shoulders the length of nylon rope he would use to lower himself back to earth using a mountaineering technique to almost bounce round the vicious obstructions.

There were no witnesses to that first triumphant ascent and Ron himself, like stout Cortez silent on a peak in Darien, was lost for words when he tried to tell his tale. Those who understood him disbelieved him and he himself was not sure how high he got. Goaded by doubters he repeated his achievement next day before a host of witnesses and it was not long before scores of local lads took up the challenge and a new sport was born.

Alas, pyloneering was, like its innovator, short-lived. Ron died later that year at the age of twenty-nine and it was only after his untimely passing that he earned the nickname "Flash". His ashes are buried at the foot of his favourite and fatal pylon. A cremation ceremony was deemed unnecessary.

Grunty Fen
Pyloneering Association
emblem.

SHADWELL HUMAN (1816-1888)

Shovel Maker

Shadwell Human's fame as the inventor of the universal folding shovel does not go unchallenged. There are earlier and compelling claimants and there is even some archaeological evidence of a broadly similar tool in use in the fens during the draining of the Bedford Level in the 18th century. But if Shadwell Human did not originate this remarkable shovel he certainly perfected it.

At first glance even the finest universal folding shovel looks like any other folding implement of its type but concealed within its hollow shaft is such a multiplicity of other tools that every human endeavour from fly-fishing to sock-darning, from major surgery to grilling kebabs, from hairdressing to calligraphy is catered for.

A household owning an authentic Shadwell Universal Folding Shovel is, theoretically, fully equipped to ice a wedding cake, repair a bicycle puncture, neuter a cat, make fire, extinguish fire, whisk eggs to the density required for meringues, tattoo any normal skin, measure earthquakes, find true north, time a boiled egg . . . the list is virtually endless.

Despite being shown at the Great Exhibition in 1851 and

being described by Queen Victoria as "a most agreeable contrivance", few Shadwell Universal Folding Shovels were made, not only because they were expensive but because they were so complex that by opening one to get out, say, a darning needle, the entire contents became loosened and were almost impossible to pack back in.

A few Shadwell Universal Folding Shovels survive intact in private hands, intact only because they have never been opened. Any that have been opened are deficient in contents and rattle irritatingly even when they are not being moved as the multitudes of spring-loaded devices within ceaselessly and automatically seek to rearrange themselves properly.

The only surviving complete Shadwell Universal Folding Shovel available to public view is in the East Anglian Museum of Cultural Curiosities and Mouth Organs at 27c Chimney Street, Great Yarmouth to which a visit is made even more worthwhile since the vast collection now incorporates the Monk Bequest of Early Salad Cream Jars, Tubs and Bottles.

The last time a Shadwell Universal Folding Shovel was recorded in use was to dig the grave of the inventor with whom it was buried in St Judas' in Grunty Fen. Local legend asserts that on quiet nights the shovel can be heard rearranging itself deep underground.

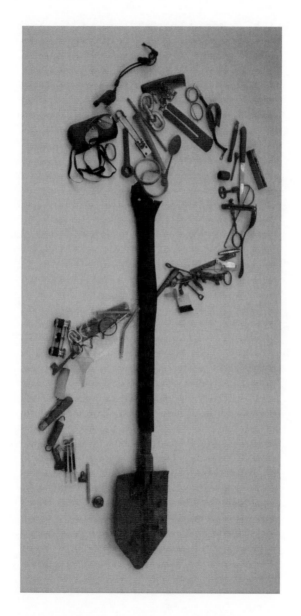

An incomplete Shadwell Universal Folding Shovel.

39

EVELYN JOBSON-BURNAGE, The Rev.

(1820-1905)

Philological lexicographer

As a divinity student at Cambridge, Evelyn Jobson-Burnage excelled in the study of Greek, Aramaic and Latin and after ordination stayed on at university to familiarise himself with Sanskrit, Old English and Low German. He had a particular purpose in mind, he recalled ruefully in his detailed memoir written in old age:

> *"With my bosom cronies, Anstruther Petres and Lancelot Pilgrim, I oftentime bespoke a pony trap of a fine summer's forenoon and would set out upon the Ely road to open our luncheon hamper, generously filled with good comestibles by the ever-faithful Mrs Benstead, en plein aire at a lushly bosky 'other Eden' yclept Grunty Fen."*

It was those happy summer picnic lunches at Grunty Fen that were to seal his fate and ruin his life.

> *"The wine flowed, the chicken was devoured, the raised pies razed until we lay back on God's green grass and dozed under a cerulean empyrean, until one or other of us would sit up suddenly, utter the words we had come to dread: 'Faces! I see faces!' and the others would sigh in unison, 'They are back! Curses and confound them! Look! They are back . . .'"*[9]

The faces were those of curious locals interested more in what the reverend picnickers were eating than who they were, and it was in fact a slice of Church Window Cake (later known as Battenberg cake) that finally brought Jobson-Burnage face to face with his first denizen of Grunty Fen. Their attempts at conversation sparked his determination to understand their language.

Convinced it was no mere pale parlance, no dialect shadow of English but a tongue unknown to scholars and like no other, he eagerly put himself forward for the living of the Parish of Grunty Fen which was almost always vacant.[10] Once installed and heedless of the ruinous state of the vicarage, he threw himself into conversation with his parishioners, urgently scribbling notes as he struggled to distinguish separate words in the guttural cascade of sound and fathom their sense.

Evelyn Jobson-Burnage.

So long as he could furnish a good supply of colourful cake, his parishioners were happy to co-operate.[11] After the first year all he could be certain of were two words: "aarryhr" for "Thanks" and "yallerupinkypie" for "cake". Progress was painfully slow because, apart from many other impediments, his flock spoke a language greatly deficient in consonants and their conversational

41

gamut was confined almost entirely to a narrow range of bodily functions which the poor parson hesitated to translate for fear of what he might find.

After ten years' painstaking research he completed the manuscript of his never-published *Lexicon and Grammar of Grunt* containing one thousand words composed mainly of vowels plus a guide to punctuation.

Exhausted by the struggle and in straitened circumstances having spent a good deal of his livelihood on coloured cake to coax conversationalists, he spent the rest of his life writing his memoir and trying to find a publisher for his *Lexicon.*

In old age, full of bitterness at having been rejected by every publisher he approached, Jobson-Burnage decided to take matters into his own hands and sank what remained of his savings into setting up his own printing-house.

However, when the movable type arrived, it contained only four letter "U"s, thus leaving him unable accurately to render the vocabulary of Grunt onto the printed page. A request to the manufacturers for more "U"s resulted in the delivery of a consignment of "V"s.

Now utterly penniless, Jobson-Burnage attempted to modify the "V"s with a treasured pickle fork inherited from his mother, but his hands were greasy from a cold supper of poached pork fat and the fork slipped, dealing him a fatal wound.

On his death bed he absolved his mother of all blame, thanked his landlady for lighting the fire in his cold garret and apologised for being unable to buy coal. She gently murmured words to the effect that he was not to worry because she had used as fuel an old scribbling book she found on his writing desk. With one gasp the wretched cleric expired.

All that now remains of his linguistic work is a single charred page of notes[12] and an early metal tape recording he made for the English Folk Tongue Society. Scholarly opinion remains divided on in which direction the tape should be played, many insisting that it sounds the same either way.

Half-consumed by flame and gnawed by rats,
the only surviving piece of the Rev. Jobson-Burnage's work.[12]

EVERSDEN MANSFIELD (1601-1660)

Natural Scientist

and **ARNOLD MANSFIELD** (1960-)

Downholsterer[13]

While the modern world still strives to save civilization with some form of safe, cheap, renewable energy, the answer may be awaiting discovery in a simple shed in the Grunty Fen area.

The origins of the Warm Bucket are long lost. Some say that like the universe itself, it was always there. But Eversden Mansfield was certainly the first to document its existence in his monograph *Ye Mysterye of ye Warme Beckit Mayde Knowne* published in 1653.

Mansfield had little education and served an apprenticeship as a downholsterer but was fired by the spirit of scientific inquiry when he inherited from his uncle, Ralph Towser of Bleak Fen, a battered brass bucket which had apparently been in the family since time immemorial.

The bucket itself is a crude affair of no great antiquarian interest. It is what lies at the bottom of the bucket that baffles the best brains. It is hard to gauge the depth of the dark substance because its glistening iridescent surface confuses the eye and makes it hard to define its place in space; however, by running a finger up the outside of the bucket it is possible to calculate the depth of the substance to be somewhere between three and four inches, varying by as much as an inch from day to day like a slowly beating heart. Furthermore, the exploratory finger also discovers a change in temperature. Even in the coldest winter the substance at the bottom of the bucket maintains a steady warmth.

In his early experiments to explore his inheritance Mansfield poked in his finger "right scared" and recorded that the substance, though sticky, thick and glutinous, fell from his skin when he withdrew his finger and left no trace except that a small wart had vanished and never reappeared.

Later research was based on the wart incident and a theory was advanced that the substance, which as its fame spread came to be known as Old Black Gip or Gype, fed on human flesh. This grotesque idea was demolished when Mansfield covered the bucket with a hermetic seal of muslin dipped in beeswax. After six months sealed off from all outside contact, the level of the Old Black Gip had actually risen by a quarter of an inch and was, if anything, slightly warmer.

Over the years the Warm Bucket has been handed down from generation to generation in the Mansfield family and it is only in recent years that the present owner, Arnold Mansfield, has made the first attempts to detach a sample of Old Black Gip for analysis.

This process must be possible since at least one other family lays claim to possessing a Warm Bucket but will not submit it to inspection or independent scientific scrutiny. (See the works of Dennis of Grunty Fen, *passim*.)

In Arnold Mansfield's case in every effort so far the Gip has always slipped off the spoon before it could be fully detached from the whole. Scissors and a professional ice cream scoop have also proved useless. Arnold himself believes the only way to succeed would be to suck some up a tube, but hesitates to do this himself and has failed to find a volunteer.

Undeterred, he dreams of the day The Warm Bucket will redeem the fortunes of humankind. Once he has devised a way of separating portions of Old Black Gip, by sucking or other means, it would be possible to initiate multiple buckets all contributing their constant warmth to some mighty generator. Or perhaps a single gigantic bucket could be built and bless the world with cheap energy for ever.

Arnold has already designed a WMB car powered by Warm Bucket technology but refuses assistance from Cambridge physicists and engineers because he fears that, as they did with atomic fusion, they would convert the bucket's power into instruments of war and tyranny. "My bucket," he has declared, quoting from his ancestor's writings, "holds the power of good or evil!"[14]

Until he has found a way to slice, scoop or suck up a sample the door to his bucket shed remains firmly locked to strangers and Arnold must follow in his forefathers' footsteps as a downholsterer.

Arnold Mansfield
renewing the security locks
on his bucket shed.

MOTHER MARJORY (fl. 1490)

Founder of the Theory of Duality of Purpose
and originator of the edible poultice

Such a complex thicket of myth, legend and folk tale surrounds Mother Marjory (or Margery or Marjorie) that it is difficult to distinguish fact from fiction. Certainly a woman called Margerie did live and flourish in the immediate Grunty Fen area in the late 15th century as evidenced by records in the *Annals of Ely* which show she was often at odds with the monks of Ely due to her radical innovations in the care of the sick at a time when the monks felt that attending to the needs of the stricken lay solely within their purview:

> *"Brother Gabriel witnesseth yat ye witch-womman Margerie hath of late called upon Elias ye molle-catcher who dyd suffer grievously from a molle-bytte to hys legge & shee dyd take unto hym a bread pudden & she dyd conjure Elias to eatte of ye pudden & shee dyd further instruct hym to lay upon hys afflicted member as a poultiss a portionne of ye bread pudden of which ye poore wretch hath bene eatting & she dyd all so tell Elias yat hee would not now gette ye lumpyblude from ye molle-bytte. By yese actionnes hath shee shewn herself contrarie to bothe holy scripture and ye wille and ordinances of my lorde Bishoppe."*[15]

However in the course of the passing centuries, any woman practising herbal medicine in her area became embraced in the Mother Marjory story much as Robin Hood is probably a syncretion of several historical figures together with a few enhancing imaginings.

Thus we may safely dismiss the narrative in which Mother Marjory fought alongside Boudicca throwing bronze buckets of black bastard beast's bane retted in goat urine at the Romans, as it is well established that metal bucket technology did not reach this area of the fens until the Middle Ages. Indeed, it was only in the mid-20th century that the bucket as an item of adornment and self-defence for ladies fully flowered, culminating in today's elegant and sophisticated buckets of which a well-dressed fen woman may require three or more in the course of a day's activities.

Right:
a plain, utilitarian
ladies' day bucket.

Left:
a highly decorated
ladies' evening bucket.

However we may say with some confidence that the medical and culinary principles embodied in the edible poultice are attributable to Marjory herself and that these principles unite all later stories attached to her legend. It may be said that Mother Marjory founded a unique school of medical research unparallelled in any other culture – that of finding a medicinal benefit from household paraphernalia. Like all great advances in medicine or the culinary arts it was based on necessity.

The extreme poverty and cramped squalor in which most fen folk lived before the arrival of the council house can scarcely be overstated. Housewives or, more properly, hovelwives, had to store food, cook, keep herbs gathered from the fields and prepare medicaments all in the most wretched conditions. Since these poor women had so little to store, the first mention of a cupboard does not occur until a report of the Society for the Relief of the Illegitimate in 1887 and when in 1931 a Scant woman was asked whether she had a draining board she thought the term applied to members of the body entrusted with the care of dykes and other ditches.

It was against this background that women, who had heard the legend of Mother Marjory in their cradles and were guided by the principle of the edible poultice, devised a strategy to better manage the use of what little they possessed. We find a brief reference in a letter written by the Rev. Eli Watkin from his parish of Much Harm cum Little Harm in 1908 describing how in an exceptionally hard January starving families survived by boiling up the bodices daubed with badger lard sewn onto children the previous November to protect their little chests from cold and damp.

In another letter he describes how his verger removed the dried eel skins used to deaden the sound of the iron wheels of the parish hearse in order to make a thin fish soup to sustain his fourteen children.

Behind many of these stories lies the constant theme of dual use. Everything in the home had to have at least two or more virtues. Pudding cloths were also slings for broken arms; bandages were also used to tie down roofing in a gale; creosote wood preservative, diluted and infused with cursing corpsewort (illustrated on p. 52), produced a liniment that served as a pick-me-up for anaemic girls as well as being rubbed into the aching calf muscle of those on the weary trudge to market to sell the famous tupping turnips sought by childless couples in Ely.[16]

Another widely used dual-purpose preparation was a

dentifrice contrived from soot and crushed woodlice which was also smeared on the face and hands by poachers to make themselves less visible at night. However, this ruse was resorted to only in the first few days after Easter when poachers traditionally washed their faces to seek absolution of their sins and were thus left vulnerable by moonlight.

Crushed woodlice occur as a general abrasive throughout the centuries. A parish record book kept in Pious End in the second half of the 18th century tells how

> *"ye preest dyd clime ye towr att mydnyte on ye feest of*
> *Al Halowes and dyd cleen ye beles with ye lyce to ye*
> *grate feere of ye dyvil and all his evel angyls"*

and the *Domestic Journal* of Mrs Anna Fetwode, wife of the Rector of Dank in 1730, records:

> *"Had all my maids a'scrubbing the earthen closets and*
> *our cutlery with wrags dipped with wodelyce paste."*

The tradition of dual use extends to the present day, even though vast improvements in domestic arrangements mean almost every home has separate storage space for food and cleaning products and the two are seldom mixed. As recently as 1994 Hannah Joslin of Wrath was reported in *The Bugle* as having perfected edible clothes pegs. Alas, her secret formula died with her. Later, in 1999, one Loftus Load of Windy Huts claimed to have invented an edible walking stick for lost travellers but until the present he has declined to give a demonstration.

So, while we may never know more about the original Mother Marjory, the power her example exerts across the centuries is quite remarkable and is deeply embedded in almost every aspect of fen life.

Sadly, the tradition is also accompanied by controversy. Just as several butchers claim to produce the original Newmarket sausages, there are at least three "original" Mother Marjory's poultices on the market. The greatest claim to authenticity may lie with Grunty Fen Women's Institute who use a recipe dating back to "before the olden days" and who supply Grunty Fen Post Office Stores.

An attempt to mass-produce edible poultices at the local patisserie factory, known as "The Fancies" (see *The Authorised Guide to Grunty Fen* p. 25) was abandoned in 2007 due to the rats.

The only recorded image of cursing corpsewort,
the plant so named because the centre of the flower head
is said to resemble a skull.

QUEENIE MARSDEN (1889-1975)

Equal rights campaigner

An avid ballroom dancing enthusiast, Queenie Marsden launched a vigorous campaign for the right of women to lead in the waltz, foxtrot etc.

Faced with ferocious opposition and inspired by the Suffragettes, she attempted to attach herself to the village hall where all dances were held. Unfortunately no part of the structure was sufficiently robust to bear the weight of her chains or even resist a little tug.

Refusing to abandon her campaign, she successfully chained herself to what is still regarded as the strongest architectural feature

Queenie Marsden's last dancing shoes.

in the village, the stink pipe outside the gents at The Bull Inn (see *The Authorised Guide to Grunty Fen* p. 20). This manoeuvre was almost instantly effective. So great was the consternation among male habitués of the bars at finding a female shrieking her ballroom propaganda close to their privy place that they found themselves not so much intimidated as inhibited.

The crunch came one night when J. Edgar Flack, visiting regional jitterbug finalist, returned to the snug from a fruitless visit to the gents and found himself quite unable to focus on his footwork during his long-anticipated St Louis Shags.

Embarrassed by the distress of their guest celebrity, the men of Grunty Fen reached a consensus permitting ladies to lead in certain specified dances at events held within the parish.

This small triumph for female emancipation opened the floodgates and ladies were soon throwing their male partners across the room when the craze for apache dancing reached Grunty Fen in the mid-sixties. Sadly, so much damage was caused to the hall and the men that the committee banned all dancing of any nature. This fell heavily not only upon Queenie, who again chained herself to the Stink Pipe, but also upon a certain Madame Winifred Poulter.

Madame Poulter, a former scenery-shifter at Sadlers Wells lately working as a scaffolder in the Ely area, had been invited to Grunty Fen by the Rev. Vernon Gumbrill to organise ballet classes as a civilizing influence for local girls. The classes had proved popular but dancing on points while wearing the only footwear most girls possessed, rubber boots, proved an insuperable obstacle. Under Madame Poulter's direction the girls were rehearsing the Dance of the Little Swans for a public concert to raise money for proper ballet shoes, but all their hopes were dashed when they were banned from the village hall.

The girls blamed Queenie Marsden who was still chained to the Stink Pipe sustained only by packets of rabbit scratchings, a local delicacy, smuggled out to her by secret admirers. Things reached a dramatic head when the Little Swans, wearing tutus made from starched nappies by their mothers, danced to The Bull and hurled abuse at Queenie, the very woman who had set out to defend dancing women's rights.

She never recovered from this humiliation and abandoned dancing to work with Madame Poulter as a scaffolder.

However, she is still remembered as a pioneer feminist admired by both sexes to the extent that many Grunty Fen men perform what they call a "Queenie", a sudden backwards step, while dancing the veleta.

Queenie Marsden, relaxing between scaffolding jobs.

NIVEN PARR (1931-)

Architect

The widespread interest taken in Grunty Fen architecture is largely
down to one man, Niven Parr, whose father, a self-employed withy
whittler, had married into a respected sprout net weaving family.
Young Niven showed an early interest in architecture, designing
and building a five-storey rabbit hutch with tromp l'oeil stained
glass windows before he was seven. Despite an undistinguished
academic career he made a close study of Cambridge College
architecture, saving anything he earned delivering mud buckets in
the village to pay for the bus fare to the city.

On leaving school he followed his father into the withy
whittling trade but would spend all his spare time wandering the
verges of the A10 looking for items that had blown off passing
building material delivery trucks. A larch-lap fence panel, a roll of
roofing felt, a sheet of marine ply or length of 4x4 would set his
imagination racing as he bore his booty home, often struggling like
a tea clipper rounding the Cape as he wove his way bearing a huge
square of plasterboard in the fen wind.

Soon remarkable sheds, faintly reminiscent of the organic
work of Antoni Gaudi, began to spring up around the family's

56

bungalow. Apparently purposeless, these sheds, none of which, alas, survived the hurricane of 1987, all bore the influence of his boyhood walks along King's Parade; the classical lines of the Senate House, the Gothic of Trinity, the towering majesty of St John's, the cool classicism of Downing or Emmanuel.

Although, with the exception of the Council Houses and the small close of executive bungalows, every structure in Grunty Fen is made almost entirely of "found" materials, often discovered in skips as well as at roadsides, young Niven's ever-growing estate of sheds attracted local admiration and even envy for their inspired originality. He had the knack of seeing the architectural possibilities in a roll of fibre-glass insulating material or a panel of garden trellis that escaped others and the time soon came when friends and neighbours who had by chance acquired, say, a gang-nailed roof truss or sheet of corrugated Perspex would consult him.

Within two years Niven gave less and less of his time to withy whittling and devoted himself almost entirely to designing not just sheds but to home extensions and even, in time, entire dwelling places.

Despite the heterogeneity of his materials, his style is instantly recognisable. Just as master mason John Wastell's overarching vision finally redeemed the confused construction of King's College Chapel, or Lancelot "Capability" Brown could with a leap of imagination see a noble landscape in a dull plain, Niven

57

had only to glance at a length of flue liner or a manhole cover to see an elegant role for it.

The arrival in the builders' merchants of moulded plastic capitals in the Doric, Ionic or Corinthian orders added a new

dimension to his work. As the wind seldom blew more than one representative of any classical order off a lorry he was invariably obliged to blend all three in a peristyle or arcade and his ability to use a dozen different historical styles in even the most modest lean-to culminated in what was probably his greatest triumph, a lattice-paned Venetian window surmounted by a gothic entablature with rococo putti in expanded polystyrene.

Niven Parr

In recent years his work has been given fresh impetus by new components: MDF, chipboard, Jewson doors, PVC window frames. Increasingly he tends towards a minimalist style of which there are several examples in a new development behind the offal sheds at Windy Huts and in his asbestos Lady Chapel at St Judas' Parish Church.

The desire to have a new kitchen fitted every few years may never reach Grunty Fen but it has had a huge effect there. Skips left overnight in urban streets are scoured by Niven and his aides who carry off the old kitchens to transform them into handsome Elizabethan manor houses or Baroque bicycle sheds far out on the fen.

The one building material Niven has set his face against is the very one for which, together with railway sleepers, Grunty Fen had been most famous – corrugated iron sheeting. He rejects what he scornfully calls "tin shacks" as "old-fashioned". For him, plastic is the future regardless of whether the scheme is Jacobean, Queen Anne, neo-brutalist or all three.

For those who wish to know more about his work, Niven Parr gives occasional talks to Grunty Fen Fine Arts Society which are well advertised in *The Grunter* (entry half a crown, free raffle).

ANNETTE "NANNY" PETIFER (1690-1740)

Pioneer industrialist

The claim to our attention of this remarkable woman rests almost entirely on oral history. Documentary evidence is vestigial although it can be said with cautious confidence that she did exist in the first half of the 18th century and that her industrial empire was centred on Grunty Fen. Yet this curiously nebulous figure is still held in something approaching awe by local people to this day and her memory is frequently invoked in conversation.

"Oywantgewupelywontmepetifer" (I would not go to Ely without my Petifer) or "'Twerepetiferdunforer" (Her Petifer was her downfall) fall easily from local lips and the widely used saying "She/he was as common as a Petifer" implies that at one time Petifers existed in great quantities yet, by implication, were always valued despite their ready availability.

The expression "He's like a man got his Petifer caught in a mangle" or, and here we rely on a rare scrap of documentary evidence from a manuscript book of sermons compiled by an early 19th century clergyman, Tobias Clanford,

"Ye foolish vergin goeth forth without her Petifer"
indicates the importance of Petifers even after the death of Nanny Petifer herself, as does *The Wily Fenman,* a cartoon published in *The Bugle Weekly Intelligencer* in 1870, some 130 years after Nanny Petifer's death (see opposite).

The same Rev. Tobias Clanford in another sermon delivered during his two-month incumbency in the parish of St Judas preaches the Parable of the Petifer and sets out how a prodigal son spent all his Petifers and returned home with none at all.

Perhaps the most compelling clues to the existence and activity of Nanny Petifer is in the blessing

"May you have as many children as Nanny made Petifers"

60

still conferred by well-wishers on newly married couples. And fen folk looking up in wonder at the night sky are heard to gasp:

"God's been as busy as Nanny Petifer!"

Sadly, none of these fragments of evidence offers any clue to the nature and use of a Petifer. All references to Petifers are based on the assumption that everyone knows what a Petifer is so any description would be supererogatory. According to a surviving catalogue dated 1949, Grunty Fen Museum of the Fine Arts, which in 1951 suffered the same fate as the library at Alexandria, had a Petifer in its collection until it was eaten by rats in the hard winter of 1947.

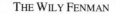

THE WILY FENMAN

Traveller (looking through telescope): "IS THAT GRUNTY FEN, MY MAN?"

Wily Fenman: "THA' IT BE. JUS' FOLLER ON A-ME."

Traveller's wife: "ARE YOU SURE I CAN GET A GENUINE PETIFER FROM THERE?"

Wily Fenman: "THA' YER CAN, MISSUS. MADE BY NANNY PETIFER 'ERSEL!"

So the only tangible evidence of this pioneer of mass production is one corner of a broken gravestone now forming part of the bicycle racks at Grunty Fen Parish Church. All that survives of its poignant and puzzling message is:

Annette Petifer . . .

1690 - 1740

Resting her fingers in Heaven

and in the church, prayers are still offered to Nanny Petifer by women who want a lot of anything.

ANNA ROMAN (?1914-2013) and others

Madame Anna Roman falls into a large category of residents of the Grunty Fen area of whom, despite their being so numerous, little is known.

In order to give a fair impression of the notable citizens of the locality and in the interest of biographical scholarship, the author includes Madame Roman and would like to mention others all of whom have little in common except their place of residence and their obscurity.

For example, during his researches, the author has repeatedly heard tell of an American called Al who trades or traded as an itinerant knife-grinder and bringer of happiness as a preacher. His grind wheel seldom spins but he attracts an active trade in his "little packets of happiness" whose virtues he preaches as he peddles from door to door, meeting an excited welcome in the poorest part of the fen ravaged by unemployment and the green flux (see August Burton, *q.v.*).

It would help the balance of this volume to know more of Mr Al as it would of Madame Roman of whom little is known except that she passed away at a very great age in 2013 in the outskirts of Lower Cur, a village only discovered in 1956, in a bungalow roofed with a cluster of onion-shaped domes commissioned from Niven Parr (*q.v.*) as one of his first projects. Oral tradition holds that she was occasionally visited by a tall chauffeur-driven lady in a toque hat and a wide choker of perfect pearls who called her "cousin".

Modelled using toilet roll tubes and Iced Gem biscuits, Anna Roman's bungalow was designed and built by Niven Parr.

The onion-domed roof is a masterpiece of architectural insight and creativity, contrived mostly from disused septic tanks.

Other examples of this genre of Grunty Fen denizens are Obergruppenführer Baron Holst von Schnickelgruber, Dud "Scarface" Pratley who flourished quietly at another recently discovered village, Great Oaf, in the 1960s and Mrs Suzanne Scarlette, known locally as "Swingdoor Suzie", who was president of Scant W.I. as late as 1975 but who vanished shortly after the raffle affair. A list of these non-native notorieties runs into a score or more all of whom found the solace of peaceful obscurity in fen fastnesses far from the hurly-burly of city life.

The author feels his work is incomplete without them and begs any reader who has relevant information to get in touch with him or, in the case of Miss Siddonie Sways, known as "Spiteful Cissie", the Ely Police.

ADRIAN SIDINGS (1925-1941)

Railway Porter and Guardian Angel

Little is known of Adrian Sidings before the day of his death, August 18th, 1941. He was then employed as a junior porter at Grunty Halt where he had been discovered as a new-born baby in 1925 resting on the steps of a signal box. He was taken in by the signalman, Ernest Doe, and raised as a railwayman with the assistance of Miss Myra Birds who performed relief duties in the box when not operating the level-crossing gates.

Adrian was named after the Emperor Hadrian by Miss Birds, who is believed to have been a Cockney. Adrian grew into a chubby young teenager largely due to his regrettable ability to extract tubes of Fruit Gums from the No.2 platform confectionery vending machine without putting a penny in the slot. It was only after Adrian's untimely death that the man employed by Messrs Rowntrees to re-fill the vending machine was able to understand why consumption of gums was so much higher at Grunty Halt than elsewhere.

On the fateful day, Adrian, who had won the hearts of all by his cheery disposition and pleasant if somewhat toothless smile, was overtaken by a sudden urge to, as he said to a colleague even as he leapt from No. 1 platform to dash across the lines to No. 2 platform, "suck one of the black ones".

His addiction to the blackcurrant-flavoured gums was his undoing.

Although only two scheduled passenger trains passed through Grunty Halt each day, the dozen men, women and children working there under Halt Superintendent Caspar Sidings (no relation)[17], were kept busy handling unscheduled freight trains bearing emergency consignments of fen celery to London to replace those destroyed in the Blitz.

On his way to the Fruit Gum machine, the unwary Adrian jumped into the path of just such a celery special and died instantly.

Grief swept the fen. A bitter tide of hatred build up against Adolph Hitler whose bombing raids in London had made the emergency celery train's journey necessary. Feelings were at a fever pitch until one day, several weeks after Adrian's death, a notice was found chalked on the booking office blackboard:

"Not Hitler. Me."

Even though Adrian had in his lifetime learned neither to read nor write, this message was widely ascribed to him. It was interpreted as an attempt from beyond the grave to relieve the Nazi dictator of responsibility and cast the entire blame for Adrian's death on himself and his exaggerated fondness for blackcurrant Fruit Gums.

From that day on, local people increasingly found signs that Adrian, who quickly attained saintly status, was still at work among them. Children arrived home from school without a trace of mud on their boots despite a morass of puddles and ditches lying in their paths. "Adrian lifted me over," they told puzzled parents. Women picking Brussels sprouts in frozen fields suddenly felt their icy fingers held in warm, gentle, invisible hands and were able to continue work after saying, "Thank you, Adrian."

Decades after his death the belief that Adrian is the Guardian Angel of the entire community is deeply rooted. No prayers are offered for Adrian's help in adversity since almost all are confident he will step in unbidden, such is his supposed watchfulness.

In his short earthly life Adrian, despite his origins and occupation, never travelled on a train because he could never afford the fare, having spent any income on Fruit Gums at the Post Office Stores when the station machines were empty. Yet he harboured another urge beyond the delights of confectionery: Adrian yearned to see more of the world. Even as a child, this son of the sidings spoke of

> *"seeing faraway places with strange-sounding names, like Barnard's Sheds, Cripple Bishop, Great Dunce and Lower Maiden".*

Almost as soon as he could walk he would wander from his sidings home and stand at the side of the lane serving Grunty Halt. There he would wave his tiny pink thumb and indulge in what he called "bike hiking", soliciting lifts from passing cyclists, there being few if any motor cars at that time.

Thus on crossbar or carrier he fulfilled his craving to see the sights, a craving which seems not to have left him even after death. Lone cyclists overtaken by darkness and lost in that labyrinth of narrow muddy lanes between precipitous ditches and dykes often report feeling a sudden jolt as if someone had mounted their machine and was indicating the road to home and safety by leaning to left or right.

67

Many an anxious family awaiting the delayed return of a young mother from the bingo at Scant will be comforted by the thought that Adrian can be relied on. And on her return, long before she kisses her family and gets their tea, the thankful woman will return to the garden gate with a tube of Rowntrees Fruit Gums in the special all-black limited edition.

In the morning the gums are gone. Wrapper and all.

Adrian Sidings, likeable lad turned Guardian Angel.

YVONNE STARVELING (1921-1959)

War heroine

In the dark days of 1940 when Britain stood alone against the Nazi war machine, Miss Yvonne Starveling was employed as an agricultural bodice trimmer at an Ely haberdasher's but each evening she would come home to Grunty Fen to put her shoulder to the wheel of the war effort. At that time every citizen was exhorted to sacrifice possessions to arm our fighting forces; like everyone else, Miss Starveling contributed her aluminium saucepans for Spitfires and the railings from her front garden for the steel industry.

But she was inspired to do more by *Angels Without Wings*, a Crown Film Unit production about the work of Army and Air Force parachutists. That night she did not sleep but set about immediately on the great work that was to be her epitaph.

For the next four years she spent every waking hour knitting parachutes from any raw material that came to hand. Despite the entreaties of her employer, she resigned from the bodice department and devoted herself entirely this self-imposed task.

Although she received no acknowledgement for the first consignment of knitted parachutes she left at the gates of a nearby

Battle of Britain airfield she assumed the airmen were too busy fighting the Germans to respond and went home to knit more.

Miss Starveling shared a problem with every other aspect of industry in that troubled time: a desperate shortage of raw materials. Having unravelled every last item of her own clothing, even sacrificing her only pair of ladderless lisle stockings, she started to beg friends and family for their help but always without fully explaining her purpose, merely specifying "the war effort" and "our intrepid flyers". Scarves, muffs, mittens, cardigans, pullovers, bobble hats, socks, dishcloths, garden string, baler twine, even Mrs Warmadam's precious family crocheted table runner and the Sculkers' treasured christening robe handed down through two generations of the family, were grist to her voracious mill.

Week after week her bales of completed parachutes were left anonymously at RAF station gates all over the area and it was only after her death that the details of her devoted patriotism became known.

A distant cousin to whom fell the duty of clearing out Miss Starveling's bungalow stumbled on her parachute account books conscientiously kept for the war years with a complete record of every parachute knitted, where it was delivered and of what it was made. A number of parachutes completed just before the war ended were also found in her sewing cupboard; Grunty Fen Women's Institute now use one as the covering for Madam

President's table when the Institute convenes and other parachutes found worthy employment dyed green and used as camouflage netting by the Scouts.

What happened to the vast number delivered to the RAF remains a poignant mystery.

Yvonne Starveling's parachute account book for 1942.

In 1959 all her parachute account books were sequestered by the government; the Ministry of Defence has repeatedly refused requests to have them reopened.

SUSAN
Dog

This selection of a mere handful of prominent persons past and present in the Grunty Fen area deals exclusively with human beings with this single exception. Susan was a dog of whom a now headless wooden memorial stands outside the gates at The Bull public house.

Even without the head, it is possible to see Susan was a huge, heavy hound. Her head has rotted away by the ceaseless supply of tasty morsels placed in her gaping jaws by well-wishers moving between the bar and the gents, as for many years it was the custom when ordering a packet of crisps, a pickled egg or one of the landlady Josie's ever-popular gourmet peanut butter sandwiches to add ". . . and one for Susan, please."

Her empty lead now hangs loosely from the lofty Stink Pipe (see *The Authorised Guide to Grunty Fen* p. 20) and her body was removed from its original position outside the gents because gentlemen kept tripping over her in the dark.

The headless wooden model of Susan,
now gradually deteriorating through age and lavish libations.

The story of the Susan Shrine takes us back to the dark days of the early 1950s when the then Vicar of Grunty Fen, Canon Hugh Crust, an exceptionally pious pastor known among his congregation as "Pi" Crust, read an article in *The Times* about the rescue work of the St Bernard dogs when Alpine snows engulfed intrepid travellers. In a visionary moment, he leapt from his study chair and expostulated:

"Why should Papist dogs have all the glory?"

He hurried to the vicarage kitchen where his thrifty wife, Hilda, was breakfasting on the remains of a large sherry trifle left over from her supper. He expostulated again:

"My dear, I have been granted a vision!"

and went on to outline a scheme to train local dogs to rescue unwary strangers as they journeyed among the perilous mires of his parish.

These mires, most of which have now been fenced off, are notoriously deceptive. Many the traveller who has stepped carelessly on what he supposed to be the shallow edge of a puddle in his path and has plunged into a sucking sump of muddy marsh sinking immediately to his waist and then, unless help is swift, slowly subsiding until vanishing altogether and forever.

These gulping puddles are left over from a formative period in local geology when entire villages were known to vanish overnight and without warning (see *The Authorised Guide to Grunty Fen* p. 2) and are really small blow holes formed as the now comparatively stable landscape digests its ancient prey as an anaconda might digest a goat.

Within weeks Canon Crust had recruited and trained a pack of local dogs which, although intellectually limited, together offered an impressive range of individual talents well beyond the normal range of sniffing and barking. They included his own dog

73

Susan, a huge, prick-eared hound with the proportions of a pony, the jaws of an alligator but the temperament of a lamb.

As a strict total abstainer from all alcoholic beverages, Canon Crust rejected the notion of tying little barrels of brandy under their chins and decided instead to provide sustenance and solace for imperilled travellers in the form of a still-famous local delicacy, Spam pasties.

Those were the days when wartime supplies of the '43 and '44 Spam were still to be found in abandoned concrete pill boxes erected as a defence measure across the fields when Hitler's hordes threated to invade (see *The Authorised Guide to Grunty Fen* p. 18).

However, early experiments showed that if the pasties were tied under the dogs' chins they could quickly lick out the Spam whereupon the pastry case collapsed and the former wearer of the pasty could also consume the fallen pieces. As his copious notes made at the time reveal, Canon Crust's solution was to tie the pasties to the back of the dogs' heads with the pointed extremities of the pasties lying longitudinally between the ears and down the nape of the neck, making it impossible for the wearer to reach them.

Thus equipped, these brave beasts were released each night to seek out any hapless souls who had strayed into a gulping mire. This worked well enough for the first few weeks although no actual rescues were effected. But then Canon Crust noticed that many of the dogs were returning each morning with their pasties missing and that Susan was putting on weight. Even so forgiving a soul as Canon Crust was forced to conclude that the sagacious Susan was seeking out other members of the canine team during their nocturnal patrol and scoffing their pasties.

So, one evening Canon Crust set out to keep watch on his hounds. After a while, Mrs Crust, who was in the public bar at The Bull distributing temperance tracts as she did most evenings, thought she heard the rattle of an expected delivery of Cyprus trifle sherry bottles outside and dashed through the bar door to investigate.

Stumbling in the darkness on the rough surface of the yard, Mrs Crust fell against the corrugated iron wall of the gents which so alarmed two gentlemen then using the facility that they let out great cries of horror and dismay believing it was another police raid. Such was the commotion that Mrs Crust became disoriented and lurched into a corner of the yard into which she would never normally have strayed because it was not far from the site of a particularly large gulping puddle.

Still clinging to the schooner of sherry she used to illustrate her homilies on abstinence, she was subsiding into the morass and was up to the corsage of cowslips her loving husband had picked for her that afternoon, when her incoherent cries were picked up by the sharp ears of Susan eating a pasty more than half a mile away across the fen. Running as fast as her weight permitted, Susan raced towards The Bull pursued by the puzzled Canon whose wife's cries were still inaudible or, at least, unintelligible to his ears.

When the Canon eventually reached the scene he found Susan had placed her huge bulk across the gaping maw of the gulping puddle making it possible for Mrs Crust to grasp her collar which still bore that night's issue of pasty. Remaining remarkably calm and seemingly unaware of the great danger she was in, Mrs Crust refused her husband's offer saying she was "quite comfortable, thank you" and contentedly ate Susan's pasty which she described as "blotting paper".

Suspecting his wife was suffering from shock, the good vicar summoned the two men who were still peering in puzzled terror from the gents and together they extracted the vicar's wife. It was only with difficulty that the saintly soul managed to persuade his spouse not to return to the bar where she insisted she wanted to rinse her corsage in gin to eradicate the stains.

Despite Susan's triumphant success on this turbulent evening, when news of the escapade reached Ely the Bishop ordered the immediate disbandment of the St Judas' Fen Rescue Dog Team and barely a year later, Susan expired when eating a dead heron she had found in a ditch.

Grateful to the dog for saving his wife's life, Canon Crust

commissioned a wooden effigy to be made by a talented local stick whittler, Pip Dazey, whose son, Cyril, still carves willow bats for Grunty Fen Cricket Club.

After Mrs Crust finally passed away in the Cambridge Clinic for Bewildered Gentlefolk the remains of the funeral wake refreshments were heaped up round the stump of Susan's memorial. Some habitués of The Bull swear they can hear them being eaten by the ghost of the deceased dog in the darkness. Others say it is rats.

The phrase "one for Susan" is still used in Grunty Fen as "one for the road" is elsewhere.

THE TARBUCK DYNASTY

Founded by Josiah Tarbuck (1808-1909), the Tarbuck dynasty made their name and fortune when the custom of wearing neckties at funerals and weddings reached first Grunty Fen in 1875 and then spread slowly to Dry Bicker, High Passion and eventually as far as Little Harm over the course of several decades.

Under pressure from their fashion-conscious wives, reluctant men submitted to this item of male apparel but their spade-like hands with massive fingers more used to pulling rhubarb in the rhubarb fields (see *The Authorised Guide to Grunty Fen* p. 28) lacked the dexterity to tie the crudest cravat even in those homes boasting the luxury of a mirror.[18]

Josiah spotted a commercial opportunity and, after mastering the art while visiting a Cambridge gentlemen's outfitter, offered to supply and tie neckwear for a small fee. At first only friends and neighbours used this novel service but news of the Tarbuck tie soon spread. Josiah would scan the marriage and death notices in *The Bugle Weekly Intelligencer* and other local media before trudging miles across the fen in all weathers with his bundle of ties purchased from an Ely outfitter slung over his shoulder. He

Josiah Tarbuck,
founder of
the Tarbuck tie business.

quickly learned that a waterproof bag made by his wife from an old American cloth table cover was preferable to the simple hessian potato sack with which he began. "It is almost impossible," he famously declared, "to get a neat knot in a wet cravat."

Josiah was already elderly when he founded the business, having for the greater part of his working life been a self-employed

78

ventriloquist and fudge vendor, but his elder son, Nathaniel, was ready to take over when his father was forced to retire suffering what we now know as repetitive strain injury in the fingers of both hands.

Under Nathaniel's guidance the business at first prospered and the resulting comfort in which the entire Tarbuck family then lived encouraged others to enter the tie trade in competition. Nathaniel was an innovator and, despite Josiah's warnings, foolishly responded to rivals by selling ready-knotted ties which could be simply slipped over the head, then, after the wedding or funeral, be loosened and removed without being untied in order to preserve the knot for future use.

This was the first step in the slow but catastrophic decline of what had been a great industry. Inevitably, families having once invested in a knot would preserve it for generations and have no further need of the Tarbuck service. In a bitter family dispute Nathaniel was finally forced by his father to hand over the business and its entire stock to his thrusting and energetic nephew, Elgin, then aged only eighteen but full of confidence he could save the situation.

Elgin began by diversifying into lavish silk cravats, and even Christmas novelty revolving bow ties which played *Jingle Bells* at random intervals and notoriously ruined an Easter vigil service at St Judas'. However, the fens were not ready for this sort of thing and the slide in profits continued. Undeterred by making a huge loss on a consignment of bombazine mourning cravats, Elgin announced a total re-branding exercise, re-launching the family business in a blaze of publicity in *The Grunter* and *The Bugle* as "Get Knotted".

Alas, this bold step was taken just as the necktie was falling out of fashion and it became acceptable for men to attend weddings and funerals with open-necked shirts as their forefathers had done.

Even worse, the family's old skills with ventriloquism and fudge had fallen into disuse and, since labour was no longer required in the rhubarb fields, the surviving members of the entire Tarbuck dynasty emigrated to what is now a bustling centre of the floss trade but was then a windswept knoll on the edge of the area known to geographers as the Great Morass. There the present generation remain in the rag trade and scratch a living knitting novelty lingerie from recycled baler twine.

STANLEY TRENCHARD-PUSEY, The Rev.

(1872-1940)

Educationist

When, in the spring of 1897, this diligent divine was first appointed to the living of Dread with St Angus-in-the-Mire, which villages have since vanished without trace, Stanley Trenchard-Pusey confessed himself profoundly shocked by the apparent brutishness of his flock steeped in superstition and evil habits.

The answer, he knew, lay in holy writ and for several years he devoted each Sunday to reading long passages from both the New and Old Testaments to his congregations without the least sign of change in their conduct. Ezekiel, Job, the First and Second Books of Samuel and the works of the Apostles failed to register other than provoking scores of purely linguistic inquiries from choirboys as to the meaning of "begat" and what happened when Adam "knew" Eve. In response he instructed each enquirer to study the Bible and discover the truth for themselves.

Only after many years of recommending Bible study to his parishioners did this good man finally have a vision of what was to be his life's work: unaware of the earlier labours of the Rev. Jobson-Burnage (*q.v.*) of St Judas' parish in Grunty Fen, he set himself the mighty task of translating the entire Bible into the local argot or dialect so that "Roof" found herself amid the "furoin cawn" and Job suffered from "arsake". After thirty years of painstaking effort while eking out his modest stipend with the help of a small grant-in-aid from the British and Foreign Bible Society and a contribution from the infant Scant Co-Operative Society whom he reluctantly allowed to insert advertisements at relevant points in the text (e.g. a mention of Co-Op ham during the Marriage Feast at Cana and a similar mention of roofing felt in the account of the construction of Noah's Ark), he was able to have his great *Fen Bible* published.

Free copies were made available not only to his own parishioners but to those of all neighbouring clerics some of whom viewed his ambitious project with some dubiety but kept their counsel as to what they viewed as the great weakness in the scheme. Trenchard-Pusey, wearied by his long labours in

translation, sat quietly in his study and awaited what he confidently expected to be the dawn of civilized conduct sweeping across the community in his cure and beyond.

Stanley Trenchard-Pusey in his wedding attire. Note the Tarbuck pre-folded and studded cravat.

Certainly the new Bibles were eagerly accepted by what he viewed as "the people who dwell in darkness" but the only sociological changes for which there was any evidence was a spectacular increase in the use of roll-your-own cigarettes among those members of his female flock who had hitherto chewed their tobacco and an inexplicable if somewhat ephemeral improvement in sanitary hygiene among both men and women.

Imagine the poor man's dismay when a colleague from Great Guttering told him the awful truth that the people were not reading the Bible even though it was now available in their own tongue because they could read no text however it might be translated. They were all without exception illiterate and although they held up their hymnals and scanned the pages during *Onward, Christian Soldiers* they were in fact chanting from memory and, as one candid cleric bluntly said, "faking it".

Thus and all-unknowing a second pastor came close to repeating the tragic failure of Evelyn Jobson-Burnage.

Yet out of this darkest of days dawned a great light. After recovering somewhat from the initial dismay that his great work was wasted, he determined to bring literacy to the fens. Largely due to his prodigious energies and refusal to surrender to the forces of ignorance, he initiated the first primary schools.

Soon the sound of chalk on slate echoed across the fen and the movement continued to spread even after his death in 1940 so that now well over half of all local children attend primary school for at least one term when their agricultural duties permit and thanks to one primary schoolmistress, Miss Eunice Turkentine of Grunty Fen, an outstanding pupil, Myra Thicknesse of Dank, gained a place at a secondary school in Ely where her manual dexterity with old copies of *The Bugle* won her a second prize for her row of sailors in the handicrafts department.

As the most successful pupil ever to emerge from one of the Rev. Trenchard-Pusey's legacy of primary schools, Myra was invited to speak at Grunty Fen Primary School prize-giving and proudly handed out awards of books to those students who had mastered their letters and tubes of Smarties to encourage those still struggling.

In her speech Myra disclosed her ambition to walk in Miss Turkentine's footsteps and become a teacher herself. That was some years ago and Myra now teaches intermediate raffia work at a Cambridge sixth-form college to those students seeking entry to the new Dank University.

As a role model for fen girls she has endowed a perpetual prize of a lavish fish supper for two to any girl entering secondary education. Furthermore, Miss Turkentine has vowed that if ever any boy shows similar academic talent an equally lavish night out at The Bull in Grunty Fen will be offered with vegetarian option.

PHILLIP TUKE-TRAYLEN (1901-1985)

Politician and campaigner

The son of a former Grunty Fen vicar, Phillip Tuke-Traylen showed an interest in public administration from an early age, publishing his first pamphlet *Whither the Fens?* at the age of fourteen. A modest and uneven work, it nevertheless shows how his mind was turning far beyond his native village to embrace a wider horizon.

Failing to find ready acceptance in any of the established political parties he stood as an independent candidate in the 1923 Parliamentary election as "Your Polite Candidate".

Broadly, his policy was to agree with anyone, especially hecklers at his well-attended meetings. Repeatedly the electorate taunted him in the hope of driving him to be impolite. They failed.

A small legacy from his father enabled him to become a full-time

*Phillip Tuke-Traylen.
"Your Polite Candidate"
ready for the hustings.*

politician without ever having to do a day's real work and although
he failed at his first and every succeeding parliamentary election,
he became famous for the vigour of his oratory, attracting huge
crowds at hundreds of meetings everywhere from Tydd Gote to
Three Holes, Wisbech to Ely and Windy Huts to Dry Bicker. No
fen community could resist the appeal of his compelling speeches.

While continuing to agree with everyone on everything, he
did develop a unique policy of his own. He resolved to improve
the image of the fens in the eyes of the nation.

Tuke-Traylen argued that the fens were unfairly held in low
esteem among other regions and needed to improve their image.
He believed that a dramatic change could be achieved by a single
measure costing next to nothing.

In a speech reported by *The Bugle* in 1951 he is quoted as
saying:

> *"Why are philanthropists, philosophers, physicians and*
> *pharmacologists treated with honour and respect? Why*
> *do these vocations attract admiration and trust? I will*
> *tell you. It is because instead of being spelled with an*
> *'f' they begin with 'ph'. So, like photography, philately*
> *and philoprogenitivism, they are taken seriously*
> *regardless of any natural virtues."*

Ignoring hecklers' shouts of "Philanderer!" and "Pharisee!"
he continued his philippic:

> *"Consider how much better, with what dignity we*
> *fenmen and our ladies would be received in the councils*

of the world if our home were known, not as The Fens
but The Phens, and we were Phenmen and
Phenwomen."

Undeterred by a leading article in that edition of *The Bugle* appearing under the headline "Phiddlesticks!" he spent the next twenty years campaigning for The Phens before retiring from public life and going to live in Philadelphia but on his death was buried in St Judas' in his native Grunty Fen under a headstone that reads defiantly:

Phillip Tuke-Traylen
Phenman

EMMANUEL PARTINGTON
VOSPER-JONES, The Rev. (1945-1999)

Clergyman and tobacconist

His diaries describe in stark terms the total horror in which the Rev. Emmanuel Partington Vosper-Jones found himself engulfed when he took up the living of St Judas', Grunty Fen, in the spring of 1970, as his first clerical appointment. Friends had warned him it was a somewhat wayward parish yet he was totally surprised to find "the extent to which it is a swamp swamped in much sin."

His parishioners, who had come to expect new pastors to be of but brief tenancy, were cool towards him. He cast round for ways to explore their lives and offer the solace of eternal salvation. Alas, they were reluctant to speak until he conceived the idea of installing a confessional box in what was then the South Aisle (now the West Aisle due to subsidence and lateral earth movement).

Lacking funds for the construction of an orthodox confessional, he was delighted when attending the village pantomime, *Babes in the Woods*, to note the scenery included a substantially constructed plywood Gingerbread House which he secured from the G.F.A.D.C. after the last performance. With very little alteration it made a serviceable confessional and was an instant success.

Queues to confess grew so long that he was obliged to institute a forward booking system which worked well enough although he was disappointed to find many parishioners booking ahead for another confession immediately after completing one. As he declared in his notes for the parish magazine, *The Grunter*:

> *"This suggests a commitment to sin and a lack of intention to do better"*

and he announced that henceforth he would accept no arrangements for confession until the sins had actually been committed.

So the queues resumed and the Rev. Vosper-Jones was

subjected to ceaseless exposure to lurid descriptions of sins whose nature he had never dreamed possible and on a scale that staggered his imagination.

Sins of the flesh predominated in an ever-increasing complexity involving permutations of personnel that left him hard put to continue adequate and appropriate responses.

Although the number and the nature of the sins confessed gave him the insight into his flock he sought, they eventually led to a complete mental breakdown and he not only resigned from the living of St Judas' after six months but left the clergy altogether and ran a tobacconist's in Gravesend where he died aged only fifty-four.

His confessional, or Gingerbread House, was removed by his successor and is still in use by Grunty Fen Academicals F.C. as a Home and Away players' toilet.

The Gingerbread House
confessional and lavatory.

GREDLEY WEAVER (1854-1880)

Philosopher

In his short life this illiterate son of a Scant goat-comber not only founded his own religious sect but probably anticipated one of the great European philosophical movements by a decade or more.

The Bugle Weekly Intelligencer for the spring of 1875 reports several sermons delivered at that time by Gredley Weaver at his Chapel of Hopeless Chaos which stood where the Basilica of Eden Wrath now stands. These contemporary reports are the only record of how far ahead of his time this unlettered artisan was: it was not until 1890 that Henri Poincaré first formulated what has come to be known as Chaos Theory and which was developed by Jacques Hadamard as late as 1898, when this approach to an understanding of the cosmos had been common currency at Grunty Fen for years.

Lacking the linguistic command of later thinkers and physicists, Weaver based his theory on a concept which generations of fen folk had referred to as a "hadnabinfer".

A had-na-bin-fer (a contraction of "if it had not been for") describes the cascade of consequences from a single small event. Edward Lorenz in his much later work drew on the example of how even a butterfly fluttering its wings might influence the path of a hurricane. For Weaver every human action, however minor it may seem, echoes down the centuries with incalculable consequences for good or ill. Even doing nothing, total inaction, has similar consequences because of future consequences avoided.

In one of his sermons Weaver tells the story of how his father, when combing a goat one day, allowed some of the animal's coat to fall inside his clothing and it was only when he changed his

vest the following spring that he found a wad of goat hair had formed close to his navel and perfectly preserved the contours of his lower abdomen. It seemed a pity to throw away this remarkable chance work of nature so it lay for some time in a saucer on his chiffonier until his wife, Doris, cut her hand when slaughtering a piglet and staunched the flow of blood with the wad of goat's hair.

The young Gredley Weaver.

Later, the doctor who stitched her wound was about to throw the bloody wad on the surgery stove when she cried, "No!" and for reasons she was at a loss to explain, buried the wad in the garden but not deeply enough for it to escape the attentions of a stray dog which, when spotted by Mrs Weaver with the wad in its mouth, dashed off across the road under a passing bus.

91

The driver stopped the bus and found the dog dead under his rear wheels with the wad still in its mouth. Mrs Weaver, with tears in her eyes, stooped to take the wad from the jaws of the dog which was reluctant to give up its prize even in death. Eventually she succeeded and buried the dog alongside the wad in her garden. From that spot there sprang a plant of a form and aspect never seen before and in autumn it bore a fruit which when soaked in gin proved a powerful aphrodisiac and shortly afterwards the famous Weaver twins, who dominated fen football for many years, were born.

But because the bus which had run over the dog was delayed while Mrs Weaver struggled to remove the wad from its jaws, one of the passengers, Lily Banks, arrived home twelve minutes late, seven minutes after her house – in which she would otherwise have already been sitting having her tea – slipped into the adjoining flooded dyke leaving her the only survivor in her family. She later remarried and her son, Clive, grew up to form with the Weaver twins one of the best forward lines Grunty Fen Academicals have ever had.

And, as Gredley Weaver pointed out in his sermon, this small, local hadnabinfer did not begin when his father let the goat hair slip down his singlet but years earlier when his grandfather, an eel-gutter, urged his son to prove himself.

"Go out and find a better job rather than spend your whole

life gutting eels like me," he urged.

So the young Weaver went to the big city to seek his fortune and when walking the streets of Ely slipped on a discarded eel skin outside the cathedral and hurt an elbow. A passing craftsman took him into his own home where his wife put his arm in a sling. To their great sorrow the couple had no child of their own to inherit their goat-combing business and, taking a liking to young Weaver, signed him up as an apprentice and potential inheritor.

All Gredley Weaver's sermons examine how all hadnabinfers branch out intricately in all directions and quite unpredictably. He told his flock:

> *"We all live in a vast hadnabinfer. There is nothing we can do to save ourselves."*

Although at first more popular than other successful sects like the Prophets of Pitiless Piety and the Warriors of Wrath, his Chapel of Hopeless Chaos sect soon so alarmed his followers that they failed to attend services and refused to leave their homes.

However, the concept of the hadnabninfer is still a central part of popular fen belief and Weaver spent the last years of his life trying to think of a form of action or inaction that had no detectable effect. He declined approaches by all the major political parties and, unlike his father, never let goat hair infiltrate his underwear.

Appendix 1: Notes on the text

Arnold Bazeley
1. "Let us not be too hasty to condemn the cruelty of the distortion of infant daughters' feet by proud parents. True, the process was torturous but consider how nimble they became in later life, hastening through all manner of muddy marshes to check the eel traps or bring in the washing. Small wonder huge dowries were demanded for marriageable females with exceptionally large feet. One woman aged 23 who had not only great feet but webbed toes withal, commanded a dowry of 24 sheets of galvanised iron, a goat and 300 Kensitas cigarettes." *(Far Afield Afoot in the Fens*, 1969, pp 401-2).

August Burton
2. Not to be confused with "The Lurch" which is a disorder with similar symptoms but has proved incurable.

Antoinette Clayden
3. Quote from the County Librarian: "I regret to have to inform members of this committee that at Grunty Fen even the greatest works of world literature are regarded as material for spills and the more monumental tomes, such as *Crockfords Clerical Directory, Debrett's Peerage Baronetage and Knightage* and *The Triumph Mayflower Owners' Club Maintenance and Spare Parts Manual* are seen simply as kindling. One of the few volumes to escape the depredations of the last hard winter was *Bannister's Illustrated Human Anatomy* and even that was eventually returned in the most wretched condition of dilapidation with grossly unseemly illustrative additions by many hands in several colours." (*Minutes of the County Libraries, Footpaths and Drains Committee*, February 17th, 1972).

Appendix 1: Notes on the text (cont.)

Chanterelle Codmonger

4. Because "they grew so fast", Chanterelle's parents named all their children after mushrooms. She has brothers Agaric, Myco and Morel and sisters Amanita, Chestnut, Button and Flat.

5. Naughty children are still commonly cowed into submission by the parental threat, "Behave yourself or I'll send for Miss Codmonger!"

6. Musicologists have identified a parallel with the arrival of the washing machine and the tea bag contributing to the decline of skiffle.

Daisy Dockerill

7. "The ladies of Grunty Fen Women's Institute at their meeting on Thursday noted the establishment of a scrapyard next to the churchyard and passed a unanimous motion condemning the fact that the profits of the enterprise would go to people living outside the village. It was further unanimously agreed that the Institute should open its own scrapyard so that the benefits would stay within the community. The meeting, which opened with the traditional singing of '*Jerusalem*' with Miss Clissold presiding at the piano, ended with a spirited rendering of '*Any Old Iron*' led by the President, Mrs Muriel Fang." (*The Bugle*, April 9th, 1948)

8. *My Life as a Modern Business Lady* by Mrs Daisy Dockerill (*The Bugle*, September 10th, 1948)

Evelyn Jobson-Burnage

9. "I, too, spoke those words of fury and regret but could never summon the spleen mustered by my fellows. For even then I knew why, time after time, I persuaded my dear friends to return to this cursed place where we knew full well we would be pestered by the

fen folk emerging like wild things from the reeds and bushes that encircled our little paradise.

"Wild faces! Rapacious eyes glinting in a green gloom. Filthy fingernails tugging at our tablecloth and withal the stench of marsh mud long rotted in primeval slime. With patience (but was it wise?) I could draw one or more of these people, for these creatures were indeed people, out into the open by offering tidbits from our feast.

"It was then, oh fell day! that I learned my first word in their tongue: 'aarryhr', betokening gratitude. For months this equivalent of 'thank you' was the only word of the language to make itself known to me but then I discovered 'yallerupinkypie', the native word for Church Window Cake. Another frustrating half-year passed before I stumbled on 'oeeruer' (Who are you?), 'eghoremaw?' (Have you got any more?) and soon I realised I was like a child standing on a beach staring out across a trackless sea of an unknown language unrelated in any way to the Indo-European family of tongues, *sui generis* here in the soggy heart of Eastern England and on the very doorstep of a great university where fine intellects proudly prated their command of all languages dead or alive."

10. "Shortly after my discovery of Grunt, for this was the name I ascribed to the true tongue of the Fen, my attention was drawn to a vacant living at Grunty Fen. The stipend was scanty, the vicarage without amenities and each of the previous three incumbents had pursued their pastoral duties for but short space, the last scarce a night. The Bishop, who had been in some despair, strained to conceal his astonished jubilation when he received the humble application of a volunteer.

"It was only many years later that I appreciated his surprise for hitherto the parish of Grunty Fen had served in the nature of a diocesan oubliette, whither erring clerics guilty of some misplacement of alms or over-familiarity with one of his flock were banished usually almost immediately to flee in haste, renouncing the cloth 'before the cock crew thrice'."

11. "Their daily diet being of a greyish hue and a somewhat sloppy consistency, they marvelled at the complex structure of my Church Window Cakes and would take them apart and strive to reassemble them like a child with a clockwork mouse. The pink and yellow of the sponge held by scarlet jam encased in saffron almond paste so held their attention that, drooling the while, they might gaze on a slice for an hour before succumbing to hunger."

12. "Oweralglavmel hoovaraw thomerly ooeraul eapieller" – *the sole surviving note from Jonson-Burnage's lost manuscript.*

Eversden Mansfield and Arnold Mansfield
13. Downholsterer: a trade similar to that of an upholsterer but confined to stuffing soft furnishings with cygnet fluff.

14. "Some seek the Holy Grail, some seek the secret of perpetual motion, and yet others seek the Philosopher's Stone. They should all cease their searching and look deep into my bucket which holds the power of good or evil. For in my Bucket Shed is the salvation of mankind, the hope of nations and eternal happiness for all. Gaze in awe into the depths of the Bucket and see the future." (Eversden Mansfield, *Letter to the Archbishop of Canterbury*, All Souls, 1652)

Mother Marjory
15. This is the first mention of the edible poultice, and the principle of the Theory of Duality of Purpose can be traced back to this record.

16. Those turnips, which still hold power over the desperate or gullible, spring naturally from Grunty Fen soil and adopt the

remarkably convincing shape of human bodies, limbs and other accoutrements in distorted or disproportionate form. They fill, in fact, the role of the mandrake root in other English cultures (*"Get with child a mandrake root"* – Donne). This branch of agriculture was outlawed under the Commonwealth but fen farmers eluded Cromwell's enforcers by dying their macabre turnips orange with a mixture of woad and hemlock and claiming they were swedes.

Braised orange turnips resembling human pudenda are still a tea time treat in many fen communities where the story of their origin is long forgotten.

Adrian Sidings

17. Sidings is a common surname in the Grunty Fen area but does not necessarily imply any family link. Sidings was the name given to or used by those people who lived in or were found in railway sidings. There are other families named in a similar vein, such as the Dranes, Hutts, Hedges, Fields and Pitts. However, the name Gutters comes from the occupation of drawing eels.

The Tarbuck Dynasty

18. "Many men and women of the poorer sort still use shallow water in a frying pan as a mirror when shaving or combing their hair but this has several disadvantages; scurf and shaving soap tends to combine with any residual fat in the pan and this necessarily somewhat opaque reflective surface of the water can, as it ripples, distort the facial image in any draught or gust shaking a house. The scurf gets stuck to chips, too." (*Customs of the Fen Folk, L. Seymour Banter, Oldways Press, 1921 p. 619*)

Appendix 2: Index of Persons

Appendix 2: Index of Persons (cont.)

Appendix 2: Index of Persons (cont.)

Appendix 3: Picture Credits

The Author wishes to acknowledge the help given with illustrating this volume by the following individuals and organisations.

Miss Edwards' Snap Album
p. 15 – Dog to egg-whisk power conversion
p. 22 – *Spirals of Love*
p. 33 – Remains of Rufus Flack's Grunty Spa
p. 35 – View up a pylon
p. 47 – Arnold Mansfield
p. 49 – Two buckets
p. 58 – Niven Parr
p. 63 – Anna Roman's onion-domed bungalow

Every Boy's Book of Wartime Wonders
p. 71 – Yvonne Starveling's parachute account book

Grunty Fen Women's Institute
p. 5   – Egg-whisk
p. 52 – Cursing corpsewort

The Lindley-Walsh Collection
p. 53 – Queenie Marsden's dancing shoes
p. 55 – Queenie Marsden
p. 85 – Phillip Tuke-Traylen

The Grosvenor-Frugal Archive of Agricultural Anthropology, Tractoriana and the Coarse Arts
p. 8   – Arnold Bazeley[†]
p. 12 – *De Rerum Horribilis Fenii Eliensis*, Dr Burton [†]
p. 16 – Cuthbert Buttress[†]
p. 17 – Austin Challis[†]
p. 24 – Patients gathering for Chanterelle Codmonger[†]
p. 25 – Cambridge rag and bone man[†]

Appendix 3: Picture Credits (cont.)

The Grosvenor-Frugal Archive of Agricultural Anthropology, Tractoriana and the Coarse Arts (cont.)

p. 29 – Dockerill advertisement
p. 36 – Grunty Fen Pyloneering Association emblem
p. 39 – An incomplete Shadwell Universal Folding Shovel
p. 41 – Evelyn Jobson-Burnage[†]
p. 43 – The charred page
p. 72 – The model of Susan
p. 78 – Josiah Tarbuck[†]
p. 82 – Stanley Trenchard-Pusey[†]
p. 89 – The Gingerbread House confessional and lavatory
p. 91 – Gredley Weaver[†]

The Sidings Family
p. 68 – Adrian Sidings[†]

British Library Flickr Commons images
p. 2 – Barry Barnard[†]
p. 30 – Rufus Flack[†]
p. 61 – Cartoon[†]

For more details of the British Library Flickr Commons images, please visit www.flickr.com/people/britishlibrary/

For more details of the British Library and its collections, please visit www.bl.uk

Back cover - the author's own photo showing him relaxing at a Grunty Fen beauty spot[†]

[†]Copyright remains with originator or image is in public domain. All other illustrations © Copyright Grunty Fennery 2015

For more about Grunty Fen, please visit
www.dennisofgruntyfen.co.uk
or email info@dennisofgruntyfen.co.uk